Strength and Conditioning
for Games Players

sports coach UK is the brand name of The National Coaching Foundation (The NCF) and has been such since April 2001.

ISBN-13: 978-1-902523-85-7
ISBN-10: 1-902523-85-7

Better Coaching...Better Sport

sports coach UK
114 Cardigan Road
Headingley
Leeds LS6 3BJ
Tel: 0113-274 4802 Fax: 0113-275 5019
Email: coaching@sportscoachuk.org Website: www.sportscoachuk.org

Patron: HRH The Princess Royal

The ideas in this text are based on the concepts in *Fitness for Games Players* by The NCF
© The National Coaching Foundation and the Sports Science Education Programme, 1996.

Author
Clive Brewer

Editor
Jennifer Smith

Proofreader
Alexis Tranter

Designer
Gavin Brearley

Acknowledgements

The author would like to thank the following for their valued contributions to the resource: Prof Mike Stone (US Olympic Committee), Mike Favre (US Olympic Committee), Dougie Bryce (**sport**scotland) and Linda Low (**sport**scotland). Thanks also go to the National Indoor Athletics Academy at Grangemouth Stadium, Grangemouth, Falkirk and to Dave Smith (GB Bobsleigh) and Rima Petlavannia (Scottish Women's Rugby) for their involvement in the photo shoot.

Cover photos courtesy of actionplus and Alan Edwards. All other photos courtesy of Alan Edwards Sports Photography, unless stated otherwise.

Coachwise Business Solutions

Produced on behalf of **sports coach UK** by

Coachwise Business Solutions
Chelsea Close
Off Amberley Road
Armley
Leeds LS12 4HP
Tel: 0113-231 1310 Fax: 0113-231 9606

Email: enquiries@coachwisesolutions.co.uk Website: www.coachwisesolutions.co.uk

scUK will ensure that it has professional and ethical values and that all its practices are inclusive and equitable

Author Profile

A director of the British Strength and Conditioning Association and in charge of **sport**scotland's athlete development programme, Clive Brewer is registered as a British Olympic Association strength and conditioning specialist. He is also a British Association of Sport and Exercise Science sports scientist and has worked with international performers from a diverse range of sports, including rugby, tennis, football and bobsleigh. Clive is a widely published author, has presented at conferences worldwide and works on national coach education programmes for **sports coach UK**, UK Athletics and various national governing bodies of sport.

Foreword

Coaches are constantly challenged to devise new methods of improving performance in their athletes. One important method of raising performance at all levels of sport is by increasing the fitness of the athletes involved. Fitness refers to specific physical, physiological and physical attributes that are directly related to a specific type of performance. On a very basic level, fitness deals with specific strength, speed, power and endurance capabilities. For example, the appropriate fitness attributes for a tennis player are quite different from those of a rugby player. Strength and conditioning (the process of achieving fitness for sport) is a multifaceted process requiring great creativity on the coach's part. Indeed, it is possible that fitness is the single most important attribute that separates winning and losing.

In recent years, recognition of the importance of fitness parameters has led to an explosion in various strength and conditioning resources and methods (as well as myths!) dealing with exactly what constitutes appropriate fitness training. It is important that the coach/athlete is able to separate scientifically founded resources from those resources that are not evidence based.

This book lays out the basic principles underlying strength and conditioning theory as well as detailed information on how to use the theory in practical applications. Furthermore, there are excellent explanations as to why different training programmes can produce different results. The information provided in this book challenges some older ideas, creates new answers to old problems and is a very practical aid for the coach/athlete in pushing the boundaries of sports performance.

Michael H. Stone

Michael H. Stone (PhD)

Director of Sports Physiology, US Olympic Committee

Inaugural Fellow of the UK Strength and Conditioning Association

Contents

Chapter 1
Introduction to Fitness Training: The Six Basic Principles

There are many recognised definitions of the concept of fitness, many of them relating to a healthy lifestyle and a person's ability to meet the demands of their environment without undue stress. In a sporting context, fitness relates to the ability to bring specific physical qualities to optimal performance. Strength and conditioning provides specific methodologies and knowledge for coaches to utilise within their sport-specific programmes, with the aim of improving physical (fitness) qualities. In the sporting arena, where teams and individuals are constantly seeking to better themselves at all levels of performance, fitness is one of the most influential and changeable elements of performance that a coach can effect. There are many approaches to developing fitness in a player. Modern sports require players to have high levels of speed, agility, strength, power and endurance in order to be effective at the top levels. These are traditionally thought to be the major components that must be developed in any sport, in order for the player to be able to perform to a reasonable level of fitness. The relationship between these major fitness components is demonstrated in Figure 1 below.

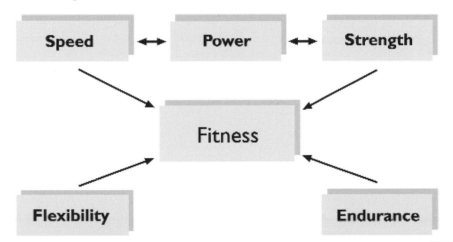

Figure 1: The major fitness components

The practical definitions of these components are outlined in Table 1 overleaf. A Glossary of terms can be found at the back of this resource to help in the overall understanding of the main concepts discussed throughout. Notes can be found on page 175.

Table 1: Defining the basic components of fitness

Component	Definition
Endurance	The ability to sustain performance. Within multiple sprint-based games, this means the ability to work repeatedly at a high intensity, recover rapidly and keep producing maximal efforts throughout the game. Conversely, in activities such as long-distance running, the ability to sustain performance will be needed over much longer periods of time, at lower (relative) intensities.
Flexibility	The range of movement possible about a joint or a series of joints.
Power	The product of work done, per unit of time, or the ability to exert a large force quickly. Work = Force x Distance Power = $\frac{\text{Distance}}{\text{Time}}$ or Force x Velocity Power is dependent upon the magnitude of the strength (force) component or the rate at which peak force can be developed (velocity component).
Speed	The ability to move the body, or part of the body, quickly.
Strength	The ability of a muscle to exert a force against a load.

This is a very simplistic view, however, as all sports require different types of speed, strength and endurance in order for athletes to be successful. This is demonstrated in Figures 2 and 3.

Figure 2: Specific fitness components of rugby union

The major fitness components of a rugby union player are power (speed x strength or force x velocity), acceleration and anaerobic endurance. This contrasts with badminton, where the major fitness components are reactions, acceleration over 5 metres, total body agility and a combination of aerobically and anaerobically produced energy.

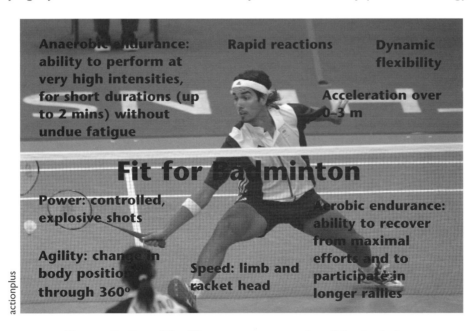

Figure 3: Specific fitness components of badminton

When a coach puts together a training and competition programme, it must consist of four major elements of preparation: technical, tactical, psychological and physical. The physical preparation component is one that can make or break a player: there is much evidence to suggest that, in top-level sport, it is the fittest and most powerful individual or team that usually wins. This may be due to the ability to perform skills more forcefully, or it may be due to the fact that, during a performance, players with better sport-specific endurance are able to replicate high-intensity plays successively, and keep producing enough energy to enable effective decisions to be made for the duration of the game.

As highlighted above, the fitness components for rugby union and badminton are different. Therefore, the training for each of these sports must be approached in a slightly different manner in order for the benefits of physical preparation to be transferred into competitive performance. Prior to establishing any training programme to improve a player's fitness, coaches should always ask themselves the following questions:

- What is the nature and type of strength, speed and power required in this sport?
- What particular energy systems (aerobic or anaerobic) need to be trained?
- What muscle groups need to be trained?
- Which muscle-fibre types should training be geared towards, ie slow-twitch (Type I), fast-twitch intermediate (Type IIa) or fast-twitch (Type IIx)?
- What type of muscle actions (isotonic, isometric) should be used?
- What would be the most appropriate strength-, speed- and power-training method for the game/player, from the range available (eg free weights and plyometrics)?

Many of these questions may not seem to make much sense at the moment. However, after reading the following chapters, the coach should be able to answer each of them and begin to identify how to put together a training programme for a particular sport, using the principles outlined to design some sport-specific practices.

It is important to remember that, when designing training programmes, there are several key principles a coach should follow in order to allow training to be successful and progressive. The principles of training outlined below allow the coach to progress training effectively. These principles should be applied to each and every form of training that the coach devises.

Overload

The overload principle states that training programmes should sufficiently stress the player's physiological mechanisms to effect an improvement. This means that working on the same programme for a long period of time will not cause a player to improve. Therefore, training status will only be improved by gradually increasing the load that the player's body is subjected to. This can be achieved by progressively altering one or more of the following:

- the **intensity** of the session (how hard the work is) – ie the work time, the rest time, the mass lifted, etc
- the **volume** of the session (how much work is done) – ie the number of repetitions that are done within a set or the number of exercises or sets that are performed
- the **frequency** of training – ie how many sessions per week are undertaken.

Coaches should remember that the stressors are cumulative: athletes need to recover from one stressor before another is applied.

Progression

Progression is a continuation of the overload principle. As the body's physiological mechanisms adapt to the training stimulus being applied, there is a need for the training to be advanced. The player will otherwise remain at a training plateau and will not respond to further training efforts. This progression has to be gradual, however, so as to prevent a player becoming injured by overexertion (or, in the longer term, overtraining) and possibly demotivated when participating in further training because the training targets are not being achieved.

Specificity

All training routines need to be tailored to the specific demands of the sport, the position being trained for and the individual needs of the player, so as to maximise the transfer of training benefits to competitive performance. The underlying factors that need to be taken into account relate to the bioenergetics of metabolism (how energy is created and supplied to the player) and the mechanical factors (musculo-skeletal requirements) involved in specific movements. Further consideration is given to each of these factors in the following chapter, where their importance in understanding performance and designing appropriate training methods is explained.

It is important for the coach to understand that not only is inappropriate training a waste of time and resources, it can be detrimental to performance.

Recovery

Physical training only provides the stimulus for physical development. The recovery period is the time when the body's physiological mechanisms for improvement are implemented. Insufficient recovery time will lead to the body becoming overtrained. This, in turn, will lead to poor performance and an increased risk of injury. If the recovery period is oversufficient, then the training effect will be lost. Chapter 8 focuses on methods that can be applied to aid recovery and therefore optimise training and performance potential.

It is important that both the coach and player realise that training/playing only provides a stimulus for improvement: it is only through rest that the body can actually improve.

Training is a stimulus that fatigues the body: it disrupts the body's normal, balanced resting state. The human body is designed to repair itself, however, and, when damage occurs, it will often repair itself to a point where it is stronger (or more efficient) than it was before. Because of this, the next training stimulus needs to be more stressful, otherwise the player's system will not be sufficiently stressed to need repairing. This is where overload and recovery integrate with one another as training principles. Adaptation and improvement can only result in improved performance ie if:

a) the training stimulus is sufficient to disrupt (overload) the player's normal homeostatic level (the normal balance of the body)

and, more importantly

b) recovery is sufficiently adequate to allow overcompensation (the technical term for the recovery of athletic potential beyond that which existed prior to the stimulus being delivered). This is explored in more detail in Chapters 8 and 9.

Therefore, if the coach allows sufficient recovery time for each physiological component in the player (eg muscles, aerobic/anaerobic system, joint structures) that was trained in a session to recover (or sufficient recovery time from a game, which stresses all the body's systems), the player's capabilities will be enhanced. Conversely, if the player trains too soon, they will not allow their bodies to recover sufficiently and the next session will commence from a fatigued state. If this pattern continues, the result will be a state of overtraining and burnout.

Variation

Variation in training is a key training principle that is often overlooked and it is where the art of coaching becomes important. It relates to how the coach manipulates when fitness training moves from general to specific in nature; how much overload to subject the player to and which methods to use; and how recovery is promoted within the player. This concept is explored in more detail in later chapters, but some general issues that need to be considered in planning variation are presented below:

• Too little progressive overload results in the player never improving.

• Too little variation in training methods or intensity will mean that it becomes very difficult to cause the player to become overloaded in training.

• Too much overload results in the player never recovering sufficiently to perform to their best potential and risks injury through overtraining.

• Too little emphasis on active recovery training and time to recover within the programme may also lead to the player underperforming and/or becoming overtrained.

Reversibility

Once the coach has mastered these training principles, the biggest challenge is to develop the training goals and the programme design. The best way to achieve this is to make the training goals all relate to testable variables. These can be monitored on a regular basis to determine whether or not a programme is working. Guidelines for testing all of the major components of fitness are found at the end of Chapters 3–7.

These implications revolve around the *use it or lose it* phenomenon. The training gains achieved will be lost if the training load is removed. Coaches therefore need to plan and control training schedules (ie around holidays or injury) so that a sufficient level of general activity is maintained to prevent detraining (reversibility) from a trained state occurring.

Implications for Coaching

Coaches need to obtain baseline data prior to commencing a training programme, as this will enable them to have a picture of where the player is currently. Training goals relating to the level of the player's skill development, and a timeframe for that development to be achieved in, can be planned from here. The next step is to take all of the scientific information that underpins effective training, and this, together with the coach's knowledge of training methods, will help develop a training programme that is effective in improving the sport-specific fitness of the games player.

Chapter 2
The Science Underpinning Training

Introduction

Coaches frequently ask, 'Why do I need to understand sports science before working on physical conditioning?' A simple analogy relates to the medical profession: doctors undertake five years of study into the science of medicine (learning the theories) before going away and practising the art of medicine. Coaching is the same: it is those who can better practise the art of applying the scientific principles who will produce the most athletically developed players.

There are two very important areas for coaches to understand if they are to effectively train their players. These are as follows:

- the bioenergic systems of the body – ie how energy is supplied and used in particular sports performance
- the neuromuscular system of the body – ie how the body is structured to execute movement and how it responds to different training stimuli.

The purpose of this chapter is to provide coaches with a working knowledge of both of these aspects of the body's functioning, so that, as the following methodological chapters are digested, the coach will have an understanding of how to adapt each of the methodologies for their particular sport.

The Energy System

The purpose of this section is to:

• identify the characteristics of each of the pathways that supply energy to the body

• recognise the importance of each energy system for training in terms of developing sport-specific training methods for players

• recognise the importance of the energy supply to a games player from a dietary perspective.

The energy currency (the factor that limits the rate at which work can be performed) of the body is called adenosine tri-phosphate (ATP). This is made up of an adenosine molecule that is chemically bonded with three phosphate molecules. These chemical bonds store energy and, when they are broken, this energy is released and used by the body to perform work.

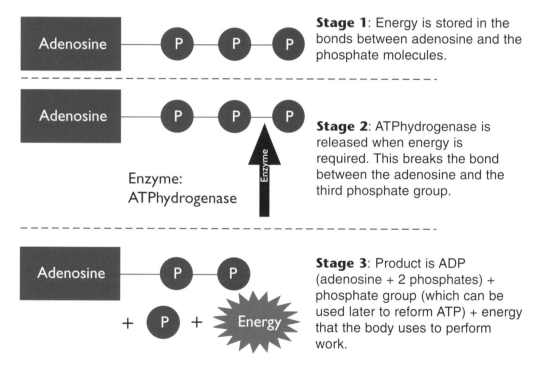

Stage 1: Energy is stored in the bonds between adenosine and the phosphate molecules.

Stage 2: ATPhydrogenase is released when energy is required. This breaks the bond between the adenosine and the third phosphate group.

Stage 3: Product is ADP (adenosine + 2 phosphates) + phosphate group (which can be used later to reform ATP) + energy that the body uses to perform work.

Figure 4: Energy is released by breaking down ATP

The body can only store a very small amount of ATP. This is used almost immediately (within seconds). ATP, therefore, has to be created by breaking down the body's energy stores. The major stores of energy in the body are in the form of blood glucose, glycogen (the muscular store of glucose) and fat. These energy stores are built up from the dietary intake of the individual.

The food that we ingest is processed and energy is taken into the body. For example, sugars enter the bloodstream and enter the muscle cells, where they are either used immediately, or are converted into glycogen, which is the muscles' energy store. What is not used or stored as muscle glycogen is then converted into fat (a high-density calorie store) within the body's adipose tissue.

Increased training puts additional demands on the body. Optimum muscle growth occurs when the energy balance is achieved.

Energy Intake   Energy Expenditure

If energy taken in is more than energy burned off, then it is necessary for the body to store energy, which it does in fat cells.

Energy Intake   Energy Expenditure

If less energy is taken in than is used by the body, the body will seek alternative sources of energy. With a normal diet, this will be found by using up fat stores. If these are not available, the body will start to break down muscle to provide energy. This is known as a catabolic state and should be avoided in games players.

Energy Intake   Energy Expenditure

Figure 5: The dietary–energy balance

It should be noted that starvation-type diets will not result in the fat stores being broken down in a player. Under such a regime, the body will necessarily conserve its high-energy storage (fat) and begin to break down muscles to provide energy. This should be avoided at all times. The safest way to lose body fat, particularly in sports players, is to increase the energy expenditure (through training) and maintain a healthy, balanced diet (see Figure 6).

It can therefore be seen that maintaining the correct energy balance is essential for a sports player if they are to have sufficient energy to perform their sport and be able to maintain low body fat levels and avoid carrying around useless excess weight in the form of fat. While fat is a high-density energy store, as will be demonstrated later in this chapter, and can provide an alternative source of energy within a normal diet, it is not a useful energy source for games players during performance due to the intensity of activity being performed.

But what is considered to be a normal diet? There are several sources of dietary information available to the coach, many of them driven by fashion or commercial companies advertising their products. Figure 6 illustrates a diet that the majority of experts would consider to be a reasonable diet for a games player.

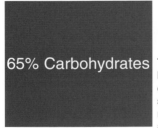

65% Carbohydrates

22% Fat

13% Protein

For healthy carbohydrates, eat rice, pasta, jacket and boiled potatoes, bread, pulses, cereals and fruit

This much fat can be found in hidden sources in the diet, so eat low-fat options, avoid sauces and pastries, eat less red meat and do not drink alcohol to excess

For sources of protein, eat white meat (lower in fat than red meat), fish, egg whites, beans, pulses, nuts and soya products

Figure 6: Recommended nutritional intake for games players

When players train for sport-specific endurance, they need to be training the metabolic pathways that deliver oxygen to the performing muscles. Therefore, it is important for a coach to understand a little about how each of these mechanisms works and its potential impact on the player.

There are three energy systems responsible for the production of ATP from the body's stores of chemical energy. These are:

• phosphagen system – sometimes referred to as the *phospho-creatine* or *creatine phosphate* system

• fast glycolysis – sometimes referred to as *anaerobic* (without oxygen) *glycolysis*

• aerobic metabolism – energy produced using oxygen.

These three energy systems are not independent of each other. Indeed, they are integrated with one another and, in any activity, energy is supplied by a combination of these systems. How they combine and which energy supply mechanism predominates in any given activity depends upon the intensity of the exercise.

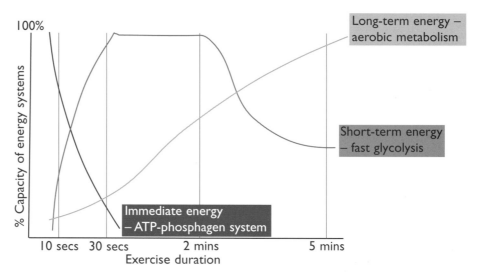

Figure 7: Energy for exercise

There is very little ATP stored in the body's cells – only enough for exercise lasting about 1–3 seconds. To compensate for this, the body is able to produce ATP via a number of different methods. As can be seen in Figure 7, very intense exercise, for durations of up to approximately 10–12 seconds, can be produced by breaking down creatine-phosphate stores in the body to produce ATP and fuel performance. However, after this duration, these stores become exhausted and energy is produced by glycolysis.

Glycolysis is the process whereby glycogen (the muscular and liver store of glucose) or glucose (if it is available in the muscle cell) is converted into a substance known as *pyruvate*. This requires 12 enzymatic reactions in total and produces a net gain of three molecules of ATP (if glycogen is broken down) or two molecules of ATP (if glucose is used) plus hydrogen (which is accepted by a carrier molecule and used at a later stage to produce more ATP in the presence of oxygen). The combined actions of the ATP-PCr (phosphagen) and glycolytic systems allow muscles to generate force when the demand for energy exceeds the rate at which energy can be supplied aerobically. In this way, these two energy systems are the major energy contributors during the early minutes of high-intensity exercise (Figure 7).

The next stage of the process depends upon the rate at which the electron transport system (see below) proceeds. In low-intensity exercise[1], where the demand for oxygen can be met by the supply, then oxygen-dependent (slow) glycolysis allows pyruvate to be transported into an organelle within the muscle cell known as a *mitochondrion*. In the mitochondria, a series of chemical reactions occurs, which ultimately produces up to 36 molecules of ATP (thus the potential total production of ATP from one molecule of glycogen is 39 molecules). This series of chemical reactions begins with the Krebs cycle, which breaks pyruvate down into a number of hydrogen atoms and electrons. These electrons then pass along an electron transport chain, producing ATP along the way. The by-products of this series of reactions are water and carbon dioxide, which are removed from the muscle cells by the blood and exhaled through the lungs. This process (known as *oxidative phosphorylation* or the *long-term energy system*) can occur for as long as the player is able to deliver glycogen to the working muscles.

When the intensity of exercise exceeds that at which there is sufficient oxygen supply[2], then oxygen-independent (fast) glycolysis becomes largely responsible for creating ATP. The end production of ATP is the same (two or three molecules), but it is the fate of the pyruvate molecule that changes the point at which the player works anaerobically. Instead of being transported into the mitochondria, pyruvate is reduced to lactate in the muscle cell.

During medium-intensity exercise, lactate is formed[3] and has two uses. When sufficient oxygen is available, lactate is transformed back into pyruvate, transported into the mitochondria and converted into 36 molecules of ATP (as described above). Alternatively, it is removed from the muscle cell, taken by blood to the liver and converted back into glucose for use as an energy store at a later stage. Following this process, it is easy to see why low- to medium-intensity exercise can be kept going for much longer periods of time.

High-intensity work, which forms the major components of the majority of games-based sports, cannot, however, be kept up for long periods of time. This can produce immediately available energy for up to 2 minutes in very fit players, but is associated with a significant fatigue component that limits how long the player can keep working anaerobically. This is because the build-up of lactate in the muscle cell is also accompanied by an increase in hydrogen ions (H^+). High concentrations of these positively charged particles make the muscle cell more acidic. Higher levels of acidity interfere with the muscle contraction mechanisms and the efficiency of the enzymes that are involved in ATP production and therefore cause fatigue.

Delayed Onset of Muscle Soreness (DOMS)

It is a common assumption among many coaches and players that a lactate build-up is responsible for the feeling of stiffness (DOMS) experienced by many players 12–48 hours after performing intense exercise activity. This is not the case. It is much more likely that this stiffness is caused by microscopic damage to the muscle tissue and the tendons/fibrous tissue that runs through muscles and connects them to bone. The feelings associated with DOMS may be exacerbated by the player performing too much static stretching, following high-intensity exercise. This is contrary to many practices, whereby coaches insist on static stretching following a training session. This concept is explored in more detail in Chapters 7 and 8.

Once lactate (and H^+) levels reach a critical value (known as the *onset of blood lactate accumulation* or OBLA point), then the player has no choice but to reduce the intensity of exercise performance if activity is to be continued.

The Implications for Training

As with all training adaptations, the mechanisms supplying energy to the working player adapt to the type of training that the player is subjected to. Generally speaking, a player's success in multiple-sprint sports (a category into which the majority of game-based sports fall) depends upon the player's ability to perform the high-intensity components of the game. The winning component that a player offers to the performance is achieved when the player is performing high-intensity activity, or is based on how often a player is able to perform high-intensity activity. It is this frequency of high-intensity activity that normally characterises a player's effectiveness in performance, rather than the amount of low-intensity work that the player performs between the high-intensity bouts.

Since the mid-1970s, exercise physiologists have promoted the idea that the only games to have a significant component of energy requirements (that are produced by oxidative phosphorylation – the oxygen-dependent long-term energy system) are badminton (which relies on this system for 10% of energy delivery), tennis (10%), soccer (20%) and lacrosse (for midfield players – 20%). This is something that is often misunderstood by coaches. For example, tennis coaches often state that players must be able to perform on court for up to 3 hours and therefore undertake endurance training to help the player to reach this goal. However, if the tennis player is not able to perform high-intensity activities repeatedly, then the coach need not worry about the game going to 3 hours, as the player will be beaten long before this time!

It is easy for a player to try to pace themselves, or reduce the intensity of their performance, in order to make sure that they *go the distance*. This is a mistake. Firstly, opponents gain a psychological advantage, as they can see that their opponent is not *firing on all cylinders* and they know that by increasing the intensity of their own performance they can win. Secondly, in a team-sport scenario, the player who is unable to contribute to the high-intensity components of the game will leave their team a player down. This can lead to scores and points being conceded and there is little point in a player being able to finish a game if, at the end, their team is three scores down.

This concept is discussed more when we move on to endurance training (Chapter 3), where specific methods for achieving the desired training effect will be introduced.

However, it is important to realise that the player must be able to work at, or near, maximal levels, recover quickly and repeat the maximal efforts, for the entire duration of the performance.

Training must therefore reflect the physiological needs of a games player. In physiological terms, the player needs:

- to be able to produce energy efficiently through the phosphagen system
- to be able to efficiently produce ATP through anaerobic glycolysis. Training at high intensities will enable the enzymes that are important in glycolysis to become more efficient at creating pyruvate and to lactate from that pyruvate very effectively
- the muscle cells to become proficient at contracting the muscle fibres and maintaining the rate of enzyme reactions in an acidic environment (the result of a build-up of lactate and H^+). This is known as lactate tolerance
- efficient mechanisms for removing lactate from the muscle cells and transporting it back to the liver for conversion back into glucose, which can then be recycled when oxygen is available
- to be able to use aerobic glycolysis and oxidative phosphorylation to produce ATP efficiently and effectively during recovery periods. These training benefits cannot be achieved by sub-maximal training efforts that occur at one pace over long distances. Training needs to be undertaken for intensities and durations that allow energy to be delivered predominantly through anaerobic pathways, with recovery periods that will facilitate the training of aerobically produced energy.

The Muscular System

The purpose of this section is to:

- identify the characteristics and structure of skeletal muscle and how this influences its function
- recognise the importance of the *all or nothing* principle of motor unit recruitment and the implications of this for force development
- identify the three types of human skeletal muscle fibre and understand the role that each of the fibres plays in sports performance
- identify the principles that govern which types of fibres are recruited and when, and the implications of this for the coach in designing a sport-specific training programme.

The bones and joints of the body provide a framework and leverage for the body. However, they cannot provide movement on their own. All functions of the body that involve movement require muscle activity. Muscle action occurs as a result of muscles changing chemical energy into mechanical energy to generate force, perform work and produce movement.

The Skeletal Muscle

The skeletal muscle is so called because it is primarily attached to bones and moves parts of the skeleton. Skeletal tissue is also called *striated* because of its alternating light and dark bands. It is a voluntary muscle tissue because it can be made to contract and relax under conscious control.

Skeletal muscles cannot actively relax: they are either contracted or they are not. Through sustained contraction and the ceasing of contraction, muscle tissue has three key functions:

- **motion** – this relies upon integration of the muscles, bones and joints
- **stabilisation** – skeletal muscle contractions maintain body (or body segment) position in a number of dynamic (changing) and static (non-moving) situations
- **thermo-regulation** – ie the regulation of body heat. Heat is a by-product of skeletal muscle contractions.

General Characteristics of Skeletal Muscle

Muscle tissue has four main characteristics that enable it to carry out its function. Firstly, it is *excitable*, which means it has the ability to respond to certain stimuli physiologically, with messages being sent from the central nervous system (the brain and the spinal cord) to the muscles. These messages are sent via the motor neurons, which in turn stimulate a movement response from the muscles. This signal causes the muscles to *contract*, which means the stimulated muscle fibres have the ability to shorten and thicken (contract), thus generating force to enable work to be done and movement to occur. Sometimes, in performing this movement, muscle fibres are stretched beyond their normal resting length. In order to achieve this, muscle fibre tissue has to be *extensible*, which means it is able to be stretched without damaging the tissue. Muscle fibres must also have *elasticity*. This is the ability of the fibre to return to its original shape after contraction or extension.

These latter principles allow the *stretch reflex* to occur in muscles. Imagine the muscle fibre as an elastic band; if you stretch it, it stores potential energy until it reaches a critical point. In muscles, this critical point is sensed by stretch receptors that detect how far and how fast a muscle fibre is being stretched. This is a safety mechanism; if the muscle is stretched too far, then, just like an elastic band, the fibre will cease to be extensible and will tear. Once the stretch receptors sense that this point is being reached in the muscle fibres, then a very strong reflex contraction will be initiated in the muscle. This stretch-reflex contraction is the basis of plyometric exercise, which will be introduced in Chapter 5.

Arrangement of Skeletal Muscle

Skeletal muscles are arranged in opposite pairs about a joint. This allows one muscle to contract and flex, and an opposing muscle to extend the joint. This opposing arrangement of muscles (or groups of muscles) allows locomotion to occur. For example, in bending (flexing) the elbow, the *Biceps brachii* [4] muscle is contracted. To extend (straighten) the elbow, the contraction in the *Biceps brachii* is stopped and the *Triceps brachii* [5] is contracted. The same principle can be observed at the knee joint, where the *Quadriceps* group[6] contracts to extend the knee and the *Hamstring* group[7] flexes the knee.

Skeletal Muscle Gross Structure

Each of the skeletal muscles in the body consists of thousands of muscle fibres. These run in parallel to each other, which means that the force of contraction can pull along the axis of the fibre. Each individual fibre is wrapped and separated from its neighbour by a fine layer of dense connective tissue. As shown in Figure 8, each fibre is then part of a bundle of up to 150 fibres (known as a *Fasciculus*), which are held together by another layer of connective fibrous tissue (the *Endomysium*). There are a number of these bundles within a muscle, each of which is surrounded and bound together by another layer of connective tissue. All of the connective tissue is tapered at both ends and blends together to form the dense, strong connective tissue known as a *tendon*. The tendons connect both ends of the muscle to the outer covering of the bone that it attaches to. This allows the force of muscle contraction to be transmitted directly from the muscle and tendons, which in turn pull on the bone at the point of attachment causing the joint and, therefore, the bone to move.

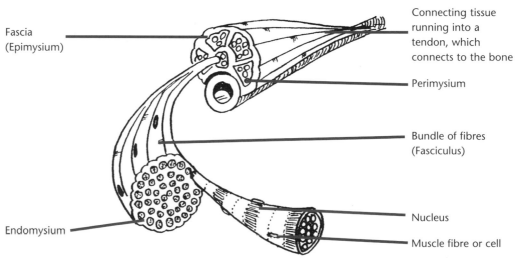

Figure 8: Muscle cross-section

Source: Farrally, M. (1995) *Introduction to the Structure of the Body*.
Leeds: Coachwise Solutions. ISBN: 1-850601-69-0

Motor Units – How Muscle Fibres Are Activated

A motor neuron (nerve) delivers an electrical stimulus to a muscle, which causes it to contract. The collective term for a motor neuron and all the muscle fibres that it innervates is a *motor unit*. One motor neuron can make contact with an average of 150 muscle fibres. This means one motor unit will cause all the muscle fibres it supplies to contract. Muscles that control precise movements have one motor unit supplying small numbers of fibres (maybe as low as two or three). Muscles responsible for powerful, gross movements have one motor unit supplying approximately 2000 muscle fibres.

It is important for coaches to realise that adjusting the number of motor units that are activated varies the strength of the resulting muscle contraction. The more force that is required, the larger the number of motor units that need to be activated.

The *All or Nothing* Principle of Muscular Contraction

As previously identified, when the central nervous system requires a movement to be carried out, an electrical signal is sent along the length of a motor neuron. However, at the end of the neuron there is a small gap between the neuron and the connective tissue that surrounds the muscle fibre. The electrical signal cannot jump directly from the nerve to the muscle; it cannot cross this gap. Instead, the neuron and the muscle communicate with each other through a chemical substance called *acetylcholine* that transmits the message from the nerve cell to the muscle cell (fibre). When a signal reaches the end of the neuron, acetylcholine (known as a *neurotransmitter*) is released and this crosses the gap between the nerve and the muscle. The amount of acetylcholine that is released is directly proportional to the strength of the neural signal; the stronger the electrical signal that travels along the nerve, the more acetylcholine is released.

Along the muscle fibre membrane are specific receptors that allow neurotransmitters to bind to them. When enough neurotransmitter binds to muscle fibre membrane, it changes the electrical potential of the membrane, giving it a positive electrical charge. There is a threshold effect in this process; if insufficient neurotransmitters are present, the electrical signal will not pass on to the muscle fibre. Until this threshold value is reached, the muscle fibre will not contract. As soon as the threshold level is reached, then the electrical impulse travels along the length of the muscle fibre and initiates the muscular contraction. This is known as the *all or nothing* principle of muscular contraction, ie motor units are either activated or they are not.

The Three Types of Skeletal Muscle Fibre

There are three types of human skeletal muscle fibre. These are characterised according to their speed of contraction and, therefore, function in human movement. This is predominantly determined by the enzyme profile of protein chains within the individual fibres, which in turn determines how fast the fibres contract, how the fibres produce energy (aerobically or anaerobically) and how well they tolerate fatigue.

Type I Fibres

These fibres are predominantly known as *slow-twitch* or *endurance* fibres. Muscles that are required to be fatigue resistant are predominantly made up of slow-twitch fibres (eg the *Gastrocnemius* and *Soleus* – the calf muscles – are predominantly slow-twitch in nature as they allow humans to stand and walk for relatively long periods of time without the muscles fatiguing). Because of the endurance nature of these fibres, they rely predominantly on energy that is produced aerobically (aerobic glycolysis and oxidative phosphorylation). As such, these fibres have a relatively slow speed of contraction. Type I fibres need a very good supply of oxygen, which in turn requires a good supply of blood. These fibres consequently have a high blood capillary to fibre ratio, causing Type I fibres to appear red when viewed through an electron microscope.

Type IIa Fibres

These are intermediate muscle fibres and are therefore also known as *fast-twitch oxidative-glycolytic* (FOG) fibres. These fibres are suited to fast, repetitive and low-intensity exercise and, because they contain large numbers of mitochondria (the organelle responsible for the aerobic production of energy), they tend to be reasonably resistant to fatigue and can recover very quickly from bouts of intense exercise. Some authorities believe these to be fast-twitch fibres that are adapted for endurance activity. This makes Type IIa ideal fibre types for games players who require explosive actions for long periods of time, with intermittent periods of recovery between.

Type IIx Fibres

Some texts will refer to these as *Type IIb fibres* but, technically speaking, these are only found in rat tissue. Type IIx muscle fibres have a very fast speed of contraction (ie they are *fast-twitch fibres* and react up to 10 times faster than slow-twitch fibres) and are responsible for very powerful, high-intensity movements. This means they have an enzyme profile that is designed to produce energy via anaerobic glycolysis. As such, they are not very resistant to fatigue and can only operate maximally for very short periods of time. Because Type IIx do not require oxygen to produce energy, they have a relatively poor blood supply and therefore will appear white when viewed under an electron microscope. Relatively speaking, players who excel in explosive movements (eg sprinters, throwers, lifters) can have very high numbers of Type IIx muscle fibres. Motor units that have predominantly fast-twitch fibres are characterised by large numbers of fibres to each motor neuron, so that large forces can be achieved very quickly by recruiting relatively small numbers of motor units.

The Size Principle of Motor Unit Recruitment

Motor units tend to be recruited by size, from small to large. Type I muscle fibres are the smallest of the muscle fibre types. These are the fibres that are recruited first in any activity. As soon as the activity requires more than approximately 25% of maximal strength, Type IIa fibres are recruited. As the activity reaches near maximal strength (power levels) or the Type I fibres fatigue (ie glycogen is no longer available as a fuel source), then the largest of the muscle fibres, the Type IIx fibres, are recruited. Force production is related to the recruitment sequence of fibres, which is dependent upon the intensity of exercise – see Figure 9.

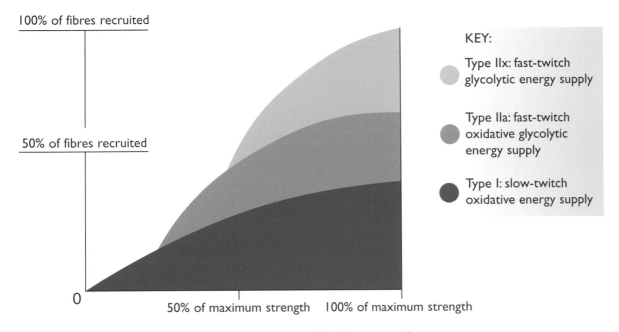

100% of fibres recruited

50% of fibres recruited

KEY:

Type IIx: fast-twitch glycolytic energy supply

Type IIa: fast-twitch oxidative glycolytic energy supply

Type I: slow-twitch oxidative energy supply

0   50% of maximum strength   100% of maximum strength

Figure 9: The size principle of muscle fibre recruitment

Coaches should note that fibre size is a relative term. Bodybuilders, who have very large muscles, are not necessarily going to have very much explosive fibre. Much of bodybuilding training is based upon developing large muscles with a good blood supply: this is not explosive muscle. Conversely, there are many very powerful sports players who do not have very big musculature: the Olympic and World Champion triple jumper, Jonathan Edwards, is a classic example of this.

Are Sprinters Born and Not Made by Training?

Maximal power output and the potential for explosive activity are very strongly determined by the proportion of fast-twitch fibres that make up a athlete's muscle. The ratio of fast-twitch to slow-twitch fibres that a person has is predominantly determined by genetics, hence the saying that a sprinter is born and not made. Coaches can influence a player's ability to be more powerful by maximising the recruitment of fast-twitch fibres by an individual, through appropriate training activities and by making the player's technique much more biomechanically efficient (eg in running). However, it is currently thought that it is not possible to create more fast-twitch fibres in an player by training: 'The coach cannot put in what God left out'. Phrased differently, you can take a donkey and make it faster but, at best, it will only be a fast donkey; it will never be a thoroughbred racehorse! Training can influence how *effectively* a games player is able to recruit and utilise their explosive fibres.

The Influence of Training on Muscle Fibres

Training influences muscle fibres and motor units in a number of different ways. One of the primary considerations for coaches of games players is the realisation that inappropriate endurance-training methods can alter the enzyme profiles of muscle fibres. Long-distance, single-paced, low-intensity running will obviously utilise aerobic energy delivery mechanisms and slow-twitch muscle fibres. Overexposure to training of this nature causes the enzyme profiles within the fast-twitch fibres to alter, so that the characteristics of the muscle become more slow twitch in nature. This can be detrimental to the games player, who relies on fast-twitch fibres in order to produce explosive power. Fortunately, with the adoption of appropriate training methods, this change is reversible over time, but prevention is better than cure. Although the total cross-section of fibre type can be increased by appropriate training, there is, unfortunately, little evidence to support the theory that training can increase the number of fast-twitch fibres that a player has. It is a case of training to maximise the fibres that are there.

The size principle of muscle recruitment illustrates to coaches that if they want to develop fast-twitch muscle fibres in their sports players, they need to be working at, or near to, maximum intensities (either in terms of movement speed or weight to be lifted) in order to develop these fibres appropriately. The ability to exert power is the objective of all games players. In any sporting situation where skill level is relatively equal (ie in normal competition), it is the most powerful team/player who will always win. Power is the ability to exert a force quickly (strength x speed). Training at maximal strength loads with an individual will not necessarily produce more power.

For example, let's assume that a tennis player has a maximal squat of 100 kilograms. If this is lifted slowly (as maximal lifts always are), they will produce less power than if they lift 70 kilograms very explosively. Both a small load lifting explosively and a heavy load accelerated slowly will recruit fast-twitch fibres.

It should also be recognised that it is the intention of the player to move a weight quickly that is the key to generating power, regardless of the weight lifted. All weights should be lifted with maximum effort and with maximum velocity if power is to be developed.

Training at these intense loads will not necessarily cause the muscles to get bigger. In beginners, the initial gains in strength that occur as a result of an intense strength-training programme are the result of the changes in the neural recruitment of motor units. Players are able to recruit more motor units more quickly and hence they are able to exert more force. Training to increase the size of muscle fibres is a specific type of strength training that will be explored more fully in later chapters.

Summary

The Energy System

- The ATP-PCr and glycolytic systems produce small to moderate amounts of ATP anaerobically and are the major energy contributors in the early minutes (typically up to 2 minutes, depending on the training state of the individual) of high-intensity exercise.

- The oxidative system uses oxygen and produces more energy than the anaerobic systems, but the delivery mechanism of the ATP is much slower.

- Carbohydrate oxidation involves glycolysis, the Krebs cycle and the electron transport chain to produce up to 39 ATP per glycogen molecule.

- When a player works anaerobically, the build-up of lactate and hydrogen ions (H^+) may cause a decrease in the efficiency of the glycolytic enzymes and interferes with the muscular contraction process. This may be a major cause of fatigue in multiple-sprint activities and/or high-intensity exercise that is 1–30 minutes in duration.

- Glycogen depletion can be a major cause of fatigue in activities that last longer than 30 minutes. Optimum nutrition and recovery protocols (see Chapter 8) can aid the recovery process for this.

- Coaches need to train the predominant energy systems that are used in their sport in order to develop effective players. This means training at high intensities, for short, intermittent durations, in order to fully develop the effectiveness of the anaerobic energy delivery mechanisms and tolerate the by-products of this method of energy delivery.

The Muscular System

- Skeletal muscle is excitable, contractible, extensible and elastic.

- Skeletal muscle can be voluntarily contracted and contractions can be voluntarily ceased, but the muscle cannot actively be relaxed.

- Connective tissue runs throughout the collection of individual muscle fibres that come together to make a muscle. This connective tissue forms the tendons, which join muscle to bone.

- A motor unit is formed from a motor neuron (nerve) and all of the muscle fibres stimulated by that neuron. Fibres within a motor unit are either contracted or not, at any given time. This is because of the *all or nothing* principle of muscle contraction.

- There are three different types of human muscle fibre. These are commonly known as Type I (slow-twitch, oxidative), Type IIa (fast-twitch, oxidative–glycolytic) and Type IIx (fast-twitch, glycolytic). These fibres are classified according to the enzyme profile of the muscle fibre, which determines the speed of contraction of the fibre and the predominant energy supply that the fibre will utilise.

- The coach should design endurance-training sessions to ensure that the appropriate fast-twitch fibres are recruited and that fibres are not, over time, encouraged to adapt to a profile that more closely resembles slow-twitch fibres.

- Efforts that require less than 25% of maximal strength will primarily recruit slow-twitch muscle fibre. For fast-twitch muscle fibres to be recruited and trained, exercises must be performed at either near-maximal strength or near-maximal speed.

Further Reading

Baechle, T. and Earle, R. (eds) (2000) *Essentials of Strength Training and Conditioning.* Illinois: Human Kinetics. ISBN: 0-736000-89-5.

Bean, A. (2003) *The Complete Guide to Sports Nutrition.* London: A & C Black. ISBN: 0-713653-89-2.*

Crosland, J. (2005) *Fuelling Performers.* Leeds: Coachwise Business Solutions/The National Coaching Foundation. ISBN: 1-902523-23-7.*

Farrally, M. (2003) *An Introduction to the Structure of the Body.* Leeds: Coachwise Business Solutions/The National Coaching Foundation. ISBN: 1-850601-69-0.*

Farrally, M. (2005) *An Introduction to Sports Physiology.* Leeds: Coachwise Business Solutions/The National Coaching Foundation. ISBN: 1-902523-65-2.*

Siff, M. (2003) *Supertraining.* Supertraining Institute. ISBN: 1-874856-65-6.

Thompson, C.W. and Floyd, R.T. (eds) (2003) *Manual of Structural Kinesiology.* New York: McGraw-Hill Education. ISBN: 0-071218-38-6.

* Available from Coachwise 1st4sport. For a full range of sports education and training equipment, please visit www.1st4sport.com or call 0113-201 5555.

Chapter 3
Endurance Training

Introduction

Sport-specific endurance is defined as the ability to sustain performance at a high intensity, recover rapidly and keep producing maximal efforts throughout the game. A well-developed cardio-respiratory system is also important in allowing the removal of waste products that build up during periods of high-intensity activity (when the body will work without oxygen, ie anaerobically). High levels of endurance allow the player to:

- continue producing maximal efforts throughout a game/match

- continue reproducing coordinated and powerful skill execution throughout a match

- continue making the best decisions throughout a performance (as fatigue interferes with concentration, increasing the likelihood of unforced errors)

- recover quickly from bouts of intense effort within a game

- recover more quickly after competitions and training, thus increasing effectiveness in subsequent training sessions and matches.

Recent debates between sports scientists, strength and conditioning specialists and coaches within British sport have centred on the need for coaches to recognise the training methods employed to reflect the specific demands of each individual sport. While specificity of training is recognised as a basic scientific requirement of any training programme, an overview of training practices among those in the field would indicate that there are many players and coaches at all levels who are not applying this training principle to their competitive preparation, particularly when it comes to endurance training.

One of the easiest ways to determine what form endurance training should take for a particular sport is to profile the needs of training for optimum competitive preparation, by analysing the physiological performance requirements of a sport, and relating these analyses to endurance-training requirements. Once this performance analysis has been undertaken, specific training ideas, designed to target the energy systems required by, for example, elite tennis players, can be introduced.

A coach can fairly easily undertake match analysis of a particular sport. Indeed, in many cases, the published data already exists and can be accessed either through an academic library or possibly the sport's governing body. If such information is not readily available, the coach simply needs to spend some time analysing a video of a game/match for their sport and complete the information in Table 2 following the instructions therein.

Table 2: A suggested method for the simple analysis of performance

Total Playing Time of Event	No. of Episodes (tally)	Duration of Each Episode	Average Duration (total duration divided by total no. of episodes)	Shortest and Longest Distances Covered at this Pace
Average time spent in competition (eg how long the ball is in play)	Square A: Insert in here one tally bar for each time the ball (for example) is in play.	Square B: Insert in here the amount of seconds that the ball is in play each time. For each tally in Square A, there needs to be a duration in Square B.	Insert in here the total no. of episodes (ie sum total of entries in Square A) divided by the total amount of time the ball was in play (ie sum total of entries in Square B).	Insert in here the shortest and the longest duration from Square B.
Working at 90–100% (maximal effort/sprinting)	Square C: Insert in here a tally bar for each time the player is working at between 90 and 100%	Square D: Insert in here the amount of seconds the player is working at 90-100%. For every tally in Square C, there needs to be a duration in Square D.	Insert in here the total no. of episodes (ie sum total of entries in Square C) divided by the total amount of time the ball was in play (ie sum total of entries in Square D). This gives an average duration for which the player is working above 90%.	Insert in here the shortest and the longest duration from Square D.
Working at 70–90% (eg fast running)	Square E: Insert in here a tally bar for each time the player is working at between 70 and 90%.	Square F: Insert in here the amount of seconds that the player is working at 70-90%. For each tally in Square E, there needs to be a duration in Square F.	Insert in here the total no. of episodes (ie sum total of entries in Square E) divided by the total amount of time the ball was in play (ie sum total of entries in Square F). This gives an average duration for which the player is working at between 70 and 90%.	Insert in here the shortest and longest duration from Square F.
Working at 50–70% (eg jogging)	Square G: Insert in here a tally bar for each time the player is working at between 50 and 70%.	Square H: Insert in here the amount of seconds the player is working at 50-70%. For each tally in Square G, there needs to be a duration in Square H.	Insert in here the total no. of episodes (ie sum total of entries in Square G) divided by the total amount of time the ball was in play (ie sum total of entries in square H). This gives an average duration for which the player is working at between 50 and 70%.	Insert in here the shortest and longest duration from Square H.
Working below 50% (walking, being stationary)	Square I: Insert in here a tally bar for each time the player is working at below 50%.	Square J: Insert in here the amount of seconds the player is working at below 50%. For every tally in Square E, there needs to be a duration in Square J.	Insert in here the total no. of episodes (ie sum total from Square I) divided by the total amount of time the ball was in play (ie sum total of entries in Square J). This gives an average duration for which the player is working below 50%.	Insert in here the shortest and longest duration from Square J.

From the table opposite, calculate the average work:rest ratio over the duration of a game/competitive event. Broadly speaking, this can be demonstrated as:

Work = Above 70%

Rest = Below 70%

This information, combined with subjective analysis of the sport (based on the coach's knowledge) will form the basis for the development of an endurance-training programme. For example, most game-based sports will require performers to repeatedly reproduce high-intensity (maximal) bouts of activity (eg rallies, sprints, contact episodes/wrestling-related activities).

By relating the intensity and duration of work to the mechanisms of energy supply, the coach can get an idea of the predominant energy supply pathways that need to be trained for a particular sport. This is a very important concept, as a player who has a well-developed aerobic metabolic pathway will not necessarily be able to cope well with periods of high-intensity work. Surprisingly, however, there is a crossover in the opposite direction, in that players who are trained to tolerate high anaerobic workloads will not necessarily have a very high $\dot{V}O_2$ max[8] but they will be able to sustain a high percentage of that $\dot{V}O_2$ max for a long period of time and work using aerobically produced energy.

Prior to looking at what methods should be applied in order to produce such an endurance-training profile, there is one more factor that needs to be taken into consideration. This relates to the effect of endurance training on muscle fibre characteristics. Most game-based sports require rapid accelerations, agility[9] and speed over distances of up to 100 metres (although more frequently over distances of 5–20 metres). These sports are also characterised by the requirement for lower- and upper-body power (force x velocity)[10] as a must for elite levels of performance. Such requirements mean the games player must be able to recruit maximum numbers of fast-twitch (Types IIa and IIx) muscle fibres (refer to Chapter 2). As detailed earlier, these fibres are characterised by their contractile speed, which is in turn enabled by their enzyme profile. Training can alter that fibre profile. Research indicates that prolonged exposure to traditional endurance training (ie sub-maximal exercise that does not involve maximal speed/force production in training) will result in the changing of fibre characteristics from Type IIx fibres to Type IIa, and Type IIa fibres to a profile that is more similar to Type I (slow-twitch, aerobic fibres). These Type I fibres have little use in power/speed development and would therefore not be desirable for multiple-sprint players.

This information should direct the coach of a multiple-sprint/high-intensity effort sport to avoid exposing players to endurance-training routines that comprise long duration, low- to medium-intensity activities. While such activities may have been thought of in the past as being beneficial to the increase of maximum oxygen uptake in players, it should be recognised that there are other means of doing this that limit adverse alterations in fibre characteristics. It is not the level of $\dot{V}O_2$ max that is important for multiple-sprint performance, but rather the highest percentage of the maximum a player can sustain.

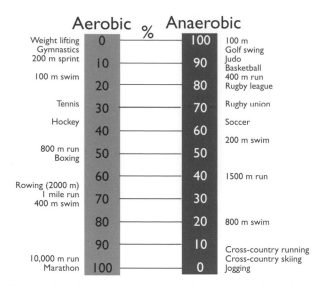

Figure 10: The energy continuum and various sports

Example 1: Tennis

Tennis is a sport that is characterised by intermittent exercise bouts of varying intensities that require immediate bursts of energy (eg a powerful serve), periods of intense activity lasting less than 10 seconds (a typical three- or four-shot point) or up to a minute (eg a 10-shot rally on a slow surface, such as clay). The nature of the tennis match is for numerous repetitive bursts of high-intensity activity, interspersed with recovery periods that, between points, must not exceed 20 seconds (Rule 30: ITF, 2000). Longer recovery breaks (maximum of 90 seconds according to rule 30) are taken between every second game and between sets.

Due to its influence on the bounce of the ball, the court surface has a big influence on the duration of the played points, with faster surfaces (eg grass) having a lower, faster bounce[11] than the slower surfaces (eg clay). Duration of played points on the faster surfaces will therefore be shorter. This analysis would indicate that training methods should reflect an intermittent period of high-intensity activity with a series of short rest breaks, with additional longer breaks that should reflect performance demand.

By relating the intensity of tennis activities to the energy supply, it can be noted that the tennis player needs to be able to produce energy via both creatine-phosphate breakdown and anaerobic fast glycolysis. Similarly, capillary lactate measurements, which indicate the build-up of toxins from anaerobic energy supply, (as undertaken by Reilly and Palmer, 1995), suggest that the major energy contributions in singles tennis are from the creatine-phosphate system[12] and aerobic metabolism of carbohydrate. Given the short duration of activity in the tennis shot, and the relatively short duration of points, it would seem that training the creatine-phosphate system and the ability to regenerate creatine-phosphate supplies (which can only happen once recovery begins) would be an important component of endurance training in tennis.

Christmass et al. (1995) demonstrated that, following the sixth change of ends, blood lactate levels reached a peak of 5.86 millimoles and that these levels remained elevated until the end of the game. This would imply that there is a significant energy contribution from anaerobic metabolism[13]. While we need to accept that playing style, opponents and court surface all significantly influence the intensity and pace of a match, it would seem apparent that endurance training should be designed to target all of the body's energy systems. Anaerobic training would need to form a significant contribution to the comprehensive preparation of players for singles tennis competition. As well as being able to produce energy anaerobically, the player must also be able to tolerate the fatiguing by-products that result from this, and this must be achieved for the duration of a match, which may last between 1 and 4 hours!

Therefore, sessions must be devised to combine high-intensity activities with recovery periods. But how long should these work and recovery periods be? This is indicated by the work:rest ratio, which can be determined by looking at some match analysis research. Reilly and Palmer (1995) found that in a three-set male tennis match there was an average of 23 (±7) games, with the ball in play for approximately 28% of the total match time. Similar results were found by Christmass et al. (1995), who found the ball to be in play for 21 minutes (23%) of a 90-minute match on a hard court surface. Further analysis by these authors revealed that, in state-level matches, the work:rest ratio was 1:1.7. Elliott et al. (1985) found a similar ratio to this, with work:rest being 1:1.8, although this changed significantly when the time it takes to change ends was built into the equation (work:rest ratio of 1:3). From these results, it would appear that endurance-training sessions need not exceed 30 minutes, with high-intensity periods of activity interspersed with rest periods on a ratio of 1 work unit to 2 rest units.

Example 2: Rugby League

It has been shown that, during an 80-minute match, forwards can cover approximately 10,000 metres; much of this is at high intensity and, as an indication of the amount of high-intensity work carried out and the time available for recovery, the work:rest ratio is 1:10 or 1:7 for the prop or hooker. Backs, on average, cover approximately 8500 metres, with a work:rest ratio of between 1:12 and 1:28 (Meir et al., 2001). This is reflected in patterns of play that coaches are familiar with. Forwards are expected to be able to break defensive lines in the first few phases of the six-tackle possession and be able to play the ball quickly enough to exploit the disrupted defence or cause an overlap for the outside backs to exploit at pace. On average, it can be seen that every 4 seconds of high-intensity activity is followed by between 30 and 80 seconds of low- to medium-intensity activity (eg moving up and back in the defensive line). Forwards work for shorter periods but are involved in the action more, whereas wingers have longer recovery periods, as they are on the fringes of the attacking/defensive line, but are expected be quicker and run further when they do get the ball.

Determining Exercise Intensity

The easiest means of determining how hard a player is working is to monitor their heart rate. Figure 11 indicates a common method of manual palpation that can be used to record heartbeats, using the first two fingers to feel the pulse. It is important to note that the thumb should not be used, as this digit has a pulse of its own. It should also be noted that heart rates are very hard to count manually when a player is working hard and there is a usual error of +10% using this method. An alternative method is to use a heart-rate monitor that uses telemetry to record heart rate on a wristwatch display. These watches make the monitoring process very easy and convenient for the player. They enable heart rate to be checked throughout a training session and provide instant feedback. Players do not necessarily all need to be using one at the same time. It is an educational process and players quickly become familiar with the level of effort and intensity required to achieve particular heart-rate training zones.

Figure 11: Manual palpation of the pulse

Maximal heart rate can only be determined by working at maximal levels. Once this is known, a training percentage can be calculated. Alternatively, a formula for calculating the theoretical heart-rate maximum can be used:

220 – age = heart-rate maximum

For example, a 25-year-old who wants to train at between 75 and 85% of heart-rate maximum would calculate:

220 – 25 = (195) x 0.75 = 146 beats per minute (bpm)

220 – 25 = (195) x 0.85 = 166 bpm

Training heart-rate range = 144–166 bpm

This is only an estimate, however, as the fitter an individual becomes, the higher their maximum heart rate. As an indicator, a player should be struggling to hold a conversation when working at 75% or above.

Endurance Training and Children

It should be remembered that children are not miniature adults and that they are often less economical in their movement. A progressive improvement in the endurance capacity begins as they enter puberty, with the onset of peak height velocity. This marks the ideal time to begin dedicated progressive endurance training with children. Prior to this, children will generally get sufficient endurance-training benefit from normal skill development and coaching activities, without additional fitness activities being dedicated to endurance work. This is particularly true if the coach is following the advice and principles outlined in the long-term athlete development (LTAD) pathway (see Stafford, 2004 for more information).

Endurance Training for Multiple-sprint and High-intensity Sports

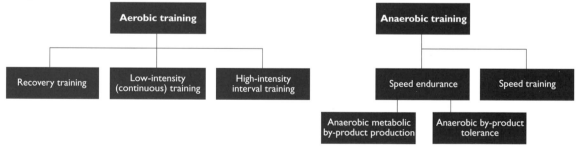

Figure 12: Training decisions chart

Endurance training can take different forms (see Figure 12); each of them can be developed to suit both the sport and the time of the competitive year. As previously identified, one of the best ways of developing a player's endurance is to work through the use of high-intensity, recovery-interval methods of training. Training at 75–85% of maximum heart rate will help to improve a player's $\dot{V}O_2$ max. This is because it improves the efficiency of the respiratory and cardiovascular systems and also leads to adaptations within muscles that will result in better use of the available oxygen. However, as has been identified, it is the players' ability to cope with higher intensity workloads that becomes important in sports performance and, at such workloads, it becomes harder for the player to continue to produce oxygen aerobically and delay the onset of anaerobic work. Delaying this onset avoids the production of toxic by-products associated with anaerobic work, which interfere with muscular contraction and contribute to fatigue in high-intensity exercise. One of the aims of endurance training must be to delay the onset of the accumulation of anaerobic by-products by increasing both the relative intensity of exercise that a player can sustain aerobically and by training the body's ability to deal with the metabolic by-products of anaerobic exercise more efficiently. Therefore, a lot of training needs to be done at a level that is close to, and above, the intensity at which these by-products of anaerobic metabolism begin to accumulate.

It is not only the improvement of $\dot{V}O_2$ max that will lead to improved performance, but the relative intensity that a player can work at, for a sustained period of time, that will enable the player to be more effective in competition.

This will enable the player to work at higher percentages of their maximum load without the fatigue associated with metabolic by-products of anaerobic work. An example of this would be lactate generation leading to acidosis in the muscle cells (refer to Chapter 2). Coaches should be aware that lactate generation can be achieved through near-maximal intensity activity with a work:rest ratio of 1:5. Tolerance for anaerobic by-products is achieved with sessions based on work:rest ratios of 1:1 to 1:3 (ie 80–100% work for between 10 and 90 seconds) – see Table 3.

Interval sessions are designed to separate periods of work and periods of active recovery. This allows the body to work more intensely (ie harder and with more quality) than is possible when working continuously. The work is still predominantly aerobic, although this can change depending upon the intensity of the work effort and the work:rest ratio. Such training can easily be manipulated to develop the high-intensity anaerobic fitness that is required in competition.

Table 3: Prescriptions for interval training

Major Energy Systems	Exercise Duration	Work:Rest Ratio	Number of Repetitions Per Set	Suggested Sets Per Workout	Intensity of Effort
Phosphagen	<10s	1:5–1:3	7–10	4–6	Maximal
ATP-PCr/ upper-end fast glycolysis	10–90s	1:5–1:2	6–8	2–5	Maximal
Lower-end fast glycolysis/slow glycolysis	90–180s	1:2–1:1	4–6	2–3	Sub-maximal (85–95%)
Aerobic	180–300s	1:1–1:0.5	3–4	1–2	Sub-maximal (75–85%)

In between work intervals, it is important that the athlete's recovery is not static, but active. This usually involves walking, but a light jog is also an option that could be considered. Active recovery serves to maintain circulation within the working muscles, ensuring a constant oxygen supply and promoting the removal of fatiguing by-products (such as lactate, hydrogen ions, etc) that accumulate during the work stages.

Fartlek Training

Some sports do not have a defined duration of play, for example, tennis and squash. Matches can take 1–4 hours to complete. Given that many players have a psychological need to feel that they can undertake longer-distance efforts (the need to be confident in meeting the challenge of playing 3-hour matches), coaches may want to intersperse sprint-based training with longer-distance work. This should, however, follow the principles outlined here and be based upon the fartlek (*speed play*) formula for training runs. Examples of fartlek training are outlined below.

Example 1
Following a dynamic warm-up:

- 3 mins steady-state running, incorporating 1 x 10-second sprint every 60 secs.
- 3 mins steady-state running, incorporating 1 x 40-metre sprint every 60 secs.
- 3 mins steady-state running, incorporating 1 x 20 secs fast, sustained running, followed by 1 x 10 secs maximal pace running.
- Repeat above 3 steps x 2.
- Cool down/stretch.

Example 2
Following a dynamic warm-up:

- Run at an easy pace for 5 mins.
- Increase pace for 3 mins (eg 75% maximum).
- Sprint for 15 secs, followed by 1 x 45-second recovery jog.
- Repeat previous step (ie sprint/jog set) for 7 repetitions (reps).
- Jog for 3 mins.
- Sprint for 10 secs, followed by 1 x 20-second recovery jog.
- Repeat sprint/jog cycle for 5 reps, with a 20-second recovery between sprints.
- Jog for 3 mins.
- 75% pace for 1 min, jog for 1 min (x 3).
- Cool down/stretch.

Long-interval Training

Long-interval training consists of running a specified number of distances, from 300–400 metres, in a given time, at about 90% maximal effort level, with short walk back recoveries or rest periods of up to 2 minutes. During this form of training it is best to work on an athletic track where the running surface is good and the distance can be measured accurately, but running around a grass park or a sandy beach[14] can be used as alternatives.

The intervals are set according to a pace dictated by maximum time over a given distance. Therefore, prior to commencing and at regular intervals during training (in order to accommodate adaptation), it is important to record the player's maximal times over these distances. The intensity of such sessions can be increased by running more intervals or by reducing the length of the rest interval.

There are many variations that are possible in developing an interval training session. If the basic principles are followed, the limitations correspond to the need for the training medium to reflect the nature of the sport on a regular basis and for the coach to introduce imaginative and useful variation to the training. Two examples of long-interval training are outlined below.

Example 1
Distance:	400 m
Pace:	75% maximum
Repetitions:	4
Sets:	3
Recovery between reps:	2 mins (walk 100 m slowly)
Recovery between sets:	4 mins

Example 2

Distance:	300 m
Pace:	85% pace
Repetitions:	5
Sets:	3
Recovery between reps:	90 secs (walk 100 m)
Recovery between sets:	2–3 mins

Short-interval Training

Short-interval sessions that consist of high-quality speed-endurance work (not speed development) can be carried out over distances of 10–150 metres. This will improve the athlete's ability to work at near-maximal speeds (important for training the fast-twitch muscle fibres and anaerobic energy systems) with specific recovery intervals.

High-intensity work is carried out at 85–100% of maximum effort (the shorter the distance, the more intense the effort needed) and is interspersed with periods of active recovery. In order to accurately calculate the correct running pace (running at a certain percentage of the maximum) 100-metre and 200-metre time trials should be used. It is important to maintain an appropriate working pace, to avoid premature fatigue.

Coaches should ensure that such sessions are scheduled for cushioning surfaces such as an athletics track, sand or grass. These surfaces provide the advantage of allowing markings that enable distances to be measured accurately.

Option 1

Distance	Reps	Sets	Recovery between Reps	Intensity
200 m	6	1	2 mins	80%
150 m	4	1	90 secs	85%
100 m	5	1	60 secs	85%

Option 2

Distance	Reps	Sets	Recovery between Reps	Intensity
130 m	4	2	90 secs	80%
180 m	6	1	90 secs	85%
120 m	4	1	90 secs	85%

Option 3

Distance	Reps	Sets	Recovery between Reps	Intensity
100 m	8	4	45 secs	80%

Option 4

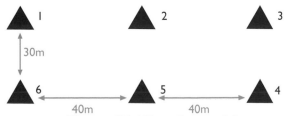

Figure 13: The glory grid

To conduct the Glory Grid drill you will need six cones and a 40-metre measuring tape.

How it works:

- Set up cones as indicated in Figure 13.
- On lap 1 the players run past cones in sequence shown at 70%.
- On lap 2 the players sprint from cones 1 to 2, 65% around rest of lap.
- On lap 3 the players sprint from 1 to 3, 65% around rest of lap.
- On lap 4 the players sprint from 1 to 4 (via 3), 65% around rest of lap.
- On laps 5 and 6 the players sprint to cones 5 and 6 respectively.
- On lap 7 the players sprint from cone 1 all the way around and back to 1.
- On lap 8 the players do a 2-minute recovery walk.
- On lap 9 the players repeat lap 7.
- On lap 10 the players repeat lap 6.
- After this, the players repeat laps 5–1 in descending order.

Notes:

- You need a definite change of pace at the start of the sprint on all laps.
- Such sessions can also be done over very short distances with the players running at 100% of their maximum.

Alternative Short-interval Training

Examples of shorter distance sessions are outlined below:

40 metres at 100%

- 3 sets of 6 x 40 m in 6–7 secs.
- 40 secs active recovery between reps.
- 2 mins active recovery between sets.

20 metres at 100%

- 2 sets of 10 x 20 m in 3–4 secs.
- 20 secs active recovery between reps.
- 1 min active recovery between sets.

Alternative Training Mediums

Most games are based on running or activities where the player is on their feet. Continually training in this fashion places impact strains on the feet, ankle and leg joints, as well as the back. Therefore, a cross-training medium is beneficial in developing endurance in a player. Two such cross-training activities are outlined, with example sessions, below.

Rowing

Sport utilises the whole body and, therefore, activities that utilise the whole body are ideal for endurance training. An example of such an activity is the rowing ergometer, which requires the cardio-respiratory system to deliver oxygen to all major muscles in the body in order to maintain workload.

Examples of rowing sessions that can be undertaken are detailed below:

Example 1: Long interval

- 3 sets of 10 mins at 75% intensity.
- 2 mins active rest between sets.

Example 2: Short interval

- 5 mins at 65% intensity.
- 4 x 5 mins at 85% intensity.
- 2 mins active rest between sets.

Example 3: Short interval

- 5 mins at 65%.
- 4 mins at 75%.
- 3 x (2 mins at 80%, 2 mins at 90%, 2 mins at 65%).
- 90 secs active recovery between sets.

Swimming

One of the problems associated with continually using running to develop endurance is that there is a repetitive stress load being applied to the musculo-skeletal structures in the legs and feet. One way of overcoming this problem, apart from the use of ergometers, is to utilise swim belts (floatation belts fitted around the player's waist) in deep water. These devices allow the player to remain upright in the water and *run* through a session without being subject to the impact forces associated with running. The sessions also have a therapeutic benefit, as the hydrostatic pressure of the water will aid muscular recovery from competitive and training stresses in a manner that no other training session can achieve. An example of such an interval session performed in the pool is detailed below.

Example 1: Running (with swim belt) interval session in the pool
- 5 mins warm-up (jogging at 65% – this will also allow the player to get used to the feeling of running in the water).
- This should be followed by 10 x 30-second sprints (with 45 secs recovery between each repetition).
- 2 mins active recovery.
- 10 x 30-second sprints (with 30 secs active recovery between each sprint).
- 2 mins active recovery.
- 10 x 15-second sprints (10 secs recovery between each rep).
- Cool-down.

If no swim-belt is available, and the player is a competent swimmer, then a swimming programme can also be an effective way of introducing variety into an interval-training programme.

Example 2: Swimming as an interval training session
- Warm-up: 200 m freestyle.
- 10 x 75 m (3 lengths) freestyle (at 100%) with 30 secs rest between sets.
- 2 mins active recovery.
- 10 x 50 m (2 lengths) 100% pace with 2:1 work:rest ratio (good swimmers should be aiming for 40 secs work to 20 secs recovery).
- 2 mins active recovery.
- 10 x 1 length freestyle (100%) going every 30 secs (or 1:1.5 work:rest ratio).
- Cool-down: 100 m of individual's choice of stroke.

The nature of the sessions described above is based on the manipulation of work intensity, in intermittent activities, to achieve high levels of match-specific endurance capabilities for the games-based sports, and all have a basis in the scientifically devised principles governing multiple-sprint activities.

Endurance Development Using Skill and Match-play Practices

Efficient use of training time is important for both the coach and the player, and combining elements of training is an ideal way to achieve this, particularly if a coach has limited time with players. Therefore, introducing endurance training to a technical coaching session is an ideal training method. If this comes at the start of the session, be aware that the player will be fatigued during later practice, which may interfere with skill/technique development. However, if the endurance training is always done at the end of training, the player will never learn to perform skills (or skills will never be tested) when fatigued, so variation on this is required within the long-term programme.

Example 1: On-court endurance training for tennis

From match analysis, it is understood that, within a match, players will get a maximum rest of 25 seconds between points and 90 seconds every other game. Coaches should also bear in mind that points between well-matched players last, on average, 5–10 seconds. Therefore, if a player is forced to return 15 fed balls to an identified target area of the court, at a ratio of 1.3–1.5 seconds per fed ball, then a 20-second work interval will be established. The player should not know how many points they will be forced to play during the interval, nor will they know how or where the next shot will be played or what the next shot will be. In this way, the conditioned practice replicates game play very closely; every shot should be played with maximum intensity.

Heart-rate monitors are excellent ways to monitor how hard a person is working. A coach can monitor a player's heart rate (HR) and compare it to a known maximum HR to see how much time a player is spending working at different percentages of the maximum.

Such sessions can last for 60 minutes, with the player being forced to take a 90-second break every 10 minutes or so.

Example 2: Defensive re-alignment development and endurance training for rugby

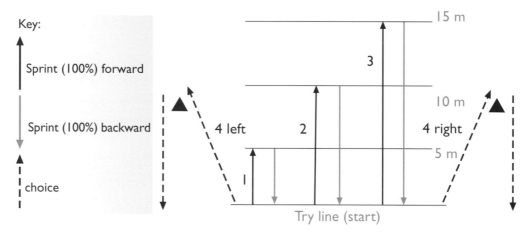

Figure 14: The defensive re-alignment development and endurance training drill for rugby

To conduct the above endurance drill, the coach will need a 15-metre measuring tape and two cones.

How it works:
- Start on the try line (start), lying on their back.
- Sprint to the 5 m line, touch with the feet, and sprint backwards to the start (point 1 in Figure 14).
- At the try line, lie on the floor so that the chest touches the ground, and get up as soon as possible.
- Sprint to the 10 m line, touch with the hand, turn and sprint back to the start line (point 2).
- At the try line, lie on the floor so that the chest touches the ground and get up as soon as possible.
- Sprint to the 15 m line (point 3), stop and do 3 x down and up*.
- Sprint back to the start line.
- Here, the coach calls 'left' or 'right', or a code word, and the player has to sprint to the diagonal cone on the 10 m line, turn around it, and sprint back to finish (point 4).

*A *down and up* involves the following: lie face down on the floor, stretch arms out to the side and legs out fully (form a star position), then stand up.

Notes:

- The drill can be made harder by putting a tackle bag at each of the lines and making the player make a tackle at each line.

- This can also be done as a communication drill, by making a line of players move through the tackles at the same time, as long as the slowest ones do not make the fastest ones lose the endurance benefit of the drill's intensity.

- Perform three sets of 4–6 reps with 20 secs between reps for elite players and up to 40 secs between reps for club players.

- Include 2 mins between sets for both levels of participant.

Example 3: Football

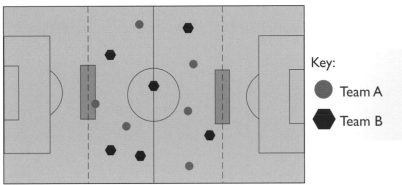

Figure 15: Six-a-side fitness game for football

How it works:
- This is a six-a-side game on a modified pitch, with no goalkeepers.

- To score, all players must be in the attacking half (or another attacking area that the coach can specify to make the players work harder).

- Two of these players must be in the goal (grey) area.

- The ball is passed into the grey area and controlled by an attacking player for a goal to be scored[15].

- The smaller the attacking area, the higher the intensity of the game.

- If one member of the defending team is not in the defending zone when a goal is scored, it is counted as double.

Testing Endurance Levels

As with other elements of a player's fitness, it is important that the coach is able to assess the endurance capabilities of their player(s). At the start of a programme, this information will provide the coach with baseline data that can be used to set the parameters for the subsequent programme and set realistic SMARTER[16] goals for the player. Tests can also be used periodically within a programme in order to determine how well a player is progressing on the training schedule set by the coach. *All* fitness tests must meet two criteria: they must be *valid* and *reliable*.

Validity relates to the ability of the test to measure exactly what it is supposed to. This is important for measuring sport-specific endurance, as there are many testing protocols that exist and can be used, but the extent to which they measure game-specific endurance needs careful consideration.

Reliability refers to the repeatability of the test. If a test is not repeatable, in that the players can undergo exactly the same procedure, under the same conditions, with the same scoring methods etc, then no direct comparisons can be made between one test and the next. The coach will therefore have no idea if any progress has been made.

The gold standard means of measuring a player's endurance capability (whether this be $\dot{V}O_2$ max or anaerobic power) is to take the player to an accredited sports science laboratory. This is impractical for all but the elite, as testing of this nature is complicated, time consuming and expensive to complete. Therefore, coaches should use field tests to obtain an objective (ie data-based) analysis of their player's endurance capabilities.

One of the best-known tests for gaining a reasonably accurate estimate of a player's $\dot{V}O_2$ max is the multi-stage fitness test (commonly referred to as the bleep test). This involves a player running between two markers placed 20 metres apart, at specifically timed intervals and with progressively increasing levels of difficulty. This commences with level 1, where the player has 8 seconds to complete the 20 metres and goes up to level 21, where the speed required makes it difficult for many to complete the distance in the time given, even if they were starting the 20-metre distance afresh!

This test has been very popular for a number of years. However, it has several limitations for sports performers. Firstly, it has been validated to estimate $\dot{V}O_2$ max. As previously explained, this is not a requirement for the games player, who needs to be able to make repeated maximal efforts without fatiguing. Secondly, the majority of the bleep test is spent running at sub-maximal paces at artificially controlled speeds, which are alien to the sportsperson and influence the efficiency of their movement. Therefore, the validity of the bleep test as a measure of the endurance capability of the athlete is very questionable.

A test does not have to produce a specific estimate of the players $\dot{V}O_2$ max or other scientific measurement. A test should be simple to set up, simple to implement and record a number that a coach can use to evaluate how the player is progressing in relation to previous tests. The test should incorporate as many sport-specific elements as possible (eg movement patterns), as long as these can be controllable by the coach.

Example 1: Anaerobic endurance shuttle test

This test has been used to assess the endurance capacities of rugby players. It involves short sprints of between 5 and 25 metres, with turning[17], running at maximal speeds and getting up and down from the floor. In order to keep the surface constant, the test will ideally be set up inside. The coach will need a 25-metre tape measure (or similar measuring device), cones, a stopwatch, a pen and the scoring sheet shown on page 35.

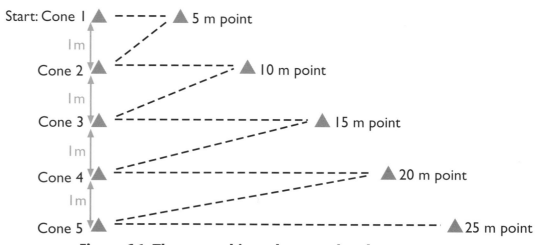

Figure 16: The anaerobic endurance shuttle test

How it works:

• The course should be marked out as illustrated in Figure 16.

• Begin at the start line (Cone 1), in a prone position (lying down on front) facing forwards.

• On the 'Go' command (start stopwatch) sprint to the 5 m point (hand touch the cone).

• Turn, sprint to Cone 2 then sprint to the 10 m point.

• Turn, sprint to Cone 3, lie prone, get up, sprint to the 15 m point.

• Repeat sets to 25 m point.

Notes:

- The player goes down onto the chest at the start, at Cone 3 and Cone 5.
- The player does a simple turn and sprint at Cones 2 and 4.
- The aim is to work at 100% and go as far as possible in 30 secs. Players must not pace themselves; this will reduce the validity of the test.
- After 30 secs, the whistle is blown and the point the player reaches is marked on the score sheet (see below) with a '1'. The set is repeated and the point the player reaches is marked with a '2', etc.
- In the example provided (Figure 17) the player manages to achieve 135 m in the first trial.
- If the player manages to complete the whole 150-metre course in 30 secs, they sprint back to cone 1 and start again.
- The stopwatch is kept running and the player walks back to start.
- After 60 secs the whistle is blown again and the player begins Trial 2.
- The 30-second work:30-second rest pattern is followed for 5 mins 30 secs, by which time the player has completed six trials and has distances recorded for each.

Total distance is calculated by adding up all the individual trial distances.

The fatigue index is calculated as a percentage of the fastest effort, as follows:

$$100 - \left(\frac{\text{Distance of shortest trial*}}{\text{Distance of furthest trial**}} \times 100 \right)$$

*should be Trial 6
**should be Trial 1

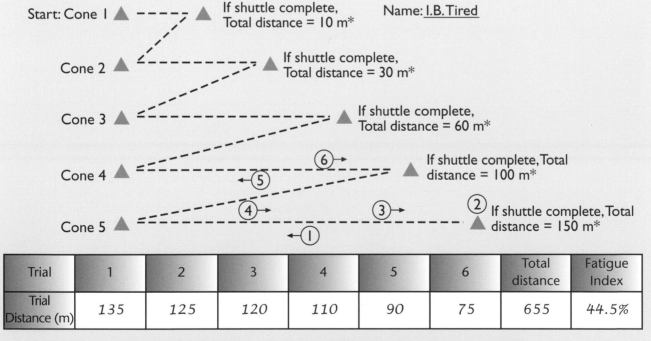

Trial	1	2	3	4	5	6	Total distance	Fatigue Index
Trial Distance (m)	135	125	120	110	90	75	655	44.5%

Figure 17: Example of the anaerobic shuttle test score sheet

* For the purposes of this exercise, total shuttle distance will disregard the slight increase caused by the diagonal return run.

Example 2: The 40-metre sprint test

This test is less intensive and is more suited to sports such as soccer, where periods of action are more intermittent. Match analysis indicates that the longest sprint a player would normally undertake in a game is 40 metres (average 17 metres), with sprinting or high-intensity action occurring once every 70 seconds. To conduct this test, a coach will require a 20-metre measuring tape, two stopwatches, two testers, a scoring chart (as below) and a pen.

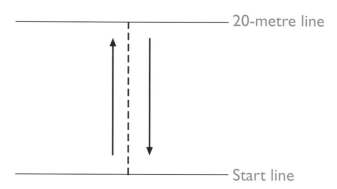

Figure 18: The 40-metre sprint test

40-metre Sprint Test Score Sheet

Sprint	1	2	3	4	5	6	7	8	9	10	Total Sprint Time
Time											

$$\text{Fatigue Index} = 100 - \left(\frac{\text{Time of slowest sprint*}}{\text{Time of fastest sprint**}} \times 100 \right)$$

*should be Sprint 10
**should be Sprint 1

How it works:

• Set the course up as illustrated in Figure 18.

• After a thorough warm-up, the players go to the start position.

• Tester 1 shouts 'Go' and immediately starts the stopwatch.

• Tester 2 immediately starts the other stopwatch, which will act as a running clock.

• Players sprint from the start line to the 20-metre line, touch it with a foot, turn and sprint back to the start line (total distance 40 m) in the fastest time possible.

• The time for Sprint 1 is recorded.

• When 50 secs show on the running clock, the players are called back to the start line.

• When 60 secs show, Tester 1 shouts 'Go' and players begin Sprint 2.

• This process is repeated, with the player starting a sprint every minute until 10 sprints have been completed.

Notes:

The coach should record total sprint time and the fatigue index, and use these to compare athlete improvement between tests.

Example 3: The 4000-metre fartlek test

With some imagination, the coach can devise other testing methods that allow the whole squad to be measured while performing simultaneously, making the process more easily adaptable for a group coaching session. The fartlek test illustrates how this can be achieved. This is a continuous test that can be employed to see how quickly players can cover a 4000-metre distance (approximately half the distance recorded for backs in rugby union or outfield players in soccer). It is important to note that this is not a test that measures how quickly a player can run 4000 metres, as this would not represent the stop-start nature of intermittent sport.

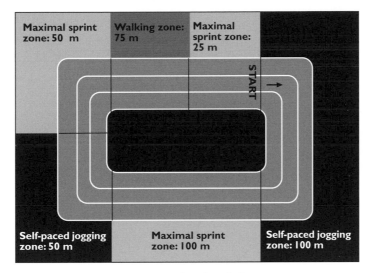

Figure 19: The fartlek test

How it works:
- Mark out a 400-metre athletics track, as identified in Figure 19.
- Following a thorough warm-up, the squad all start together on the start line.
- On the coach's 'Go' command, the players run around the track (in the direction indicated by the arrow).
- In the areas marked for maximal sprints, the players must run as fast as they possibly can.
- In the self-paced areas, they can choose how quickly they wish to go.
- In the walking zone, the players are not allowed to overtake squad members. They can go as slow as they want to, but *cannot overtake* someone else who is in front of them (in this zone only). This means that, as in a game when they are required to work sub-maximally *off the ball*, they are forced to work a bit harder to get the best result (ie the best possible time).
- The coach should record the total time taken for 10 laps (ie 4000 m).

Notes:
- The objective is to complete the 4000 m in the fastest possible time, applying the above, zoned conditions.
- As a result, in the first part of the test they work as hard as they can, in the mid-part they work as hard as they want to, and in the final part their work rate is determined by someone else.
- The coach can record, with one stopwatch, the total amount of time that it takes each player to complete the test.

Summary

Appropriately designed endurance training for games players should facilitate:

• increased cell myoglobin content, increased capillary density and number of mitochondria for improved transport of oxygen to the cell and improved utilisation of oxygen within the muscle

• Increased efficiency of the cardio-vascular system for increased stroke volume per beat, increased cardiac output and increased waste product removal

• increased muscle glycogen stores

• enhanced quality and function of muscle fibres, particularly fast-twitch fibres

• increased activity of enzymes that are involved in the process of producing energy aerobically and anaerobically from glucose and glycogen

• improved resistance to fatigue during high-intensity exercise

• enhanced multi-directional speed of movement.

Coaches should base their endurance-training sessions upon an analysis of their particular sport.

Coaches can achieve overload in an interval training session by manipulating any of the following:

• the duration of the work interval

• the mode (walk, jog) and length of the rest interval (both factors are determined by the predominant work:rest interval)

• the intensity of the work interval (determined by the energy supply mechanism that is predominant for the individual sport)

• the total volume of work done (remembering that more is not necessarily always better).

Efficient coaching practice involves incorporating endurance drills into training sessions and combining them with skill- and/or situation-specific practices. When designing these practices, the coach should be guided by their imagination and the scientific principles governing the energy supply requirements and work:rest ratios for their sport.

Tests for sport-specific endurance should be repeatable, interpretable, easy to implement and measure, and should test the individuals' capabilities to perform the endurance requirements of the sport in question.

References

Christmass, M.A., Richmond, S.E., Cable, N.T. and Hartmann, P.E. (1995) 'A metabolic characterisation of singles tennis' in *Science and Racket Sports II* (1998) Lees, A., Maynard, I., Hughes, M. and Reilly, T. (eds). London: E. and F.N. Spon. ISBN: 0-419230-30-0.

Elliott, B., Dawson, B. and Pyke, F. (1985) 'The ergogenics of singles tennis', *Journal of Human Movement Studies* 11: 11–20.

International Tennis Federation (2000) *Rules of Tennis*. London: ITF Ltd.

Meir, R., Colla, P. and Milligan, C. (2001) 'Impact of the 10-meter rule change on professional rugby league: implications for training.' *Strength and Conditioning Journal* 23 (6): 42–6.

Reilly, T. and Palmer, J. (1995) 'Investigation of exercise intensity in male tennis single/lawn tennis' in *Science and Racket Sports II*, Lees, A., Maynard, I., Hughes, M. and Reilly, T. (eds). London: E. and F.N. Spon. ISBN: 0-419230-30-0.

Further Reading

Siff, M. (2003) *Supertraining*. Supertraining Institute. ISBN: 1-874856-65-6.

Stafford, I. (2004) *Coaching for Long-term Athlete Development*. Leeds: Coachwise Business Solutions/The National Coaching Foundation. ISBN: 1-902523-70-9.*

To purchase wristwatch monitors, as mentioned in the Determining Exercise Intensity section of this chapter, please contact Coachwise 1st4sport at the points of contact below.

For other resources on the LTAD method, please contact Coachwise 1st4sport.

---

* Available from Coachwise 1st4sport. For a full range of sports education and training equipment, please visit www.1st4sport.com or call 0113-201 5555.

Chapter 4
Developing Strength and Power

Introduction

There have probably been more misconceptions about the role of strength training in sport, and the products of strength training, than any other element of fitness training. This chapter addresses some of the common misconceptions, demonstrates that strength and power training is a fundamental underpinning of all sports, and provides coaches with guidelines for specific exercises that will promote sport-specific strength.

Strength

Strength is the ability of the muscle to exert a force against a load. It has a vector quantity, in terms of application direction of the force and magnitude of application of that force. The force that is created is a result of the contraction of specific muscles. Strength gain in the muscles (as a result of appropriate training) is specific to the angle of the joint at which training has occurred.

Strength is important in game-based sports to:

- enhance performance by allowing the more forceful application of skills
- act as a basis for long-term power development
- aid in the prevention of contact and non-contact injuries.

However, before designing a sport-specific strength-training programme, the coach needs to understand the answers to the following questions:

- What is the nature of strength or power required?
- What joint actions (and therefore what muscle groups) need to be trained?
- What type of muscle actions are involved?
- What is the most appropriate method to use in order to achieve the desired objectives?

Sport-specific technique can be considered to be the result of the appropriate application of the developed force, which is a product of strength and motor control. Such motor control is developed through the nervous system and appropriate strength training has been shown to lead to improved neuromuscular efficiency that aids performance in biomechanically similar movements (Stone, 2000). Functional strength is therefore related to being strong in the normal movement patterns for a player in their particular sporting situation.

Power

Strength is also the precursor to power, which is probably the most important characteristic that a games player can develop. This can best be described as the product of work done per unit of time, or the ability to exert a large force quickly.

Work = Force x Distance   Power = $\frac{\text{Work}}{\text{Time}}$ or Force x Velocity

Power is therefore dependent upon the magnitude of the strength component, which may be a primary determinant in contact-oriented sports, such as rugby. It is also dependent upon the speed component, which will be the key factor in sports where power is determined by the velocity component, such as tennis (racket-head speed) or soccer (Figure 20).

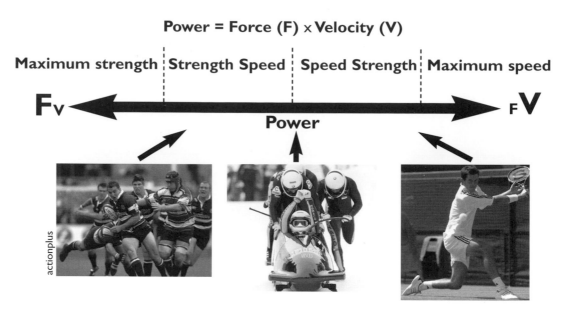

Power = Force (F) × Velocity (V)

Maximum strength | Strength Speed | Speed Strength | Maximum speed

F_V ← → $_FV$

Power

Figure 20: The force–velocity continuum

Force

Force generation is determined by Newton's second law:

Force = Mass x Acceleration

Acceleration is important as this results in velocity, which is the vital component of power. It is also very important to realise that the rate at which force is developed (RFD) is associated with acceleration capabilities in athletes and this can be a determining factor in generating superior athletic performance. Most critical aspects of sports performance occur in very short time frames (<250 milliseconds). If athletes can be trained to produce greater forces within that time frame, then greater accelerations, and therefore velocities, can be achieved. Hence, the ability to produce force (strength) and its related component, RFD, is an integral part of power production and as such, may be a key component in determining athletic success.

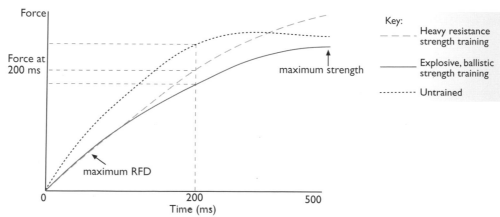

Figure 21: Force production as a result of training type[18]

Figure 21 shows the rate of force development (RFD) and force at 0.2 seconds for untrained (solid line), heavy-resistance trained (dashed line) and explosive-ballistic trained (dotted line) subjects.

The Importance of Sport-specific Strength and Power Training

The concept of strength training should be very specific to the nature of the sport that the athlete is being conditioned for. Most sports require higher levels of power and acceleration rather than absolute strength or increased muscle bulk. For example, force is applied for 0.08–0.2 seconds during the ground-support phase of running, whereas peak force production requires up to 0.6–0.8 seconds in dynamic movements. Even in largely non-ballistic movement activities, such as cycling, rowing or swimming, performance is usually determined by the ability to generate force quickly and thereby achieve a critical force output, more often than not within the 0.2-second timeframe. Therefore, in order to be effective, training methods need to be based around exercises that develop maximal force in gross muscle structure, in minimal amounts of time, because most sports rely on large groups of muscles working together to execute skilful movements.

As illustrated in Figure 21, a performer who is untrained cannot generate a large overall force, particularly when compared to someone who has undertaken resistance training designed to promote maximum strength. However, if you compare the rate of force development that is achievable up to, and at, 200 milliseconds with untrained and maximum-strength-trained performers, there is not much difference between them. In a sportsperson who has been trained using methods designed to promote explosive strength, however, it can be seen that, although the maximum amount of force that can be generated is much less than in someone who has undertaken heavy-resistance strength training, the rate of force production is significantly greater, particularly at the vital 200 millisecond point. This makes explosive-strength training a very real and highly relevant underpinning component of a sportsperson's training programme.

There is significant evidence to indicate the efficacy of using high-force, high-velocity, movement-specific training exercises in order to produce superior performance gains in strength-/power-oriented sports (Stone, 2000). In all sports, the biggest training priority (ie factors that primarily influence winning and losing) is strength and speed (power). In any given situation, it is usually the most physically powerful team/individuals who will predominate. This has been backed up by a number of studies in the USA (Stone, 2002) which have compared performance measures with power, both in the short term and long term, and which demonstrate a strong positive association between maximum strength, sports performance and related variables. Also, given that stronger athletes tend to be more powerful, it is safe to hypothesize that more powerful athletes are better performers. Therefore, performers should strive to become as strong as possible within the context of their sport (Stone, 2002). Imagine being a defender in soccer and trying to mark a centre forward who has the ability to jump 1 metre off the ground, or playing against a netball player who can rapidly explode a pass the length of the court, or a tennis player who can consistently serve at 125 mph.

Movement Analysis: Sport and Training Movements

Games-based sports are based on strength, power and practice at sport with movement-specific patterns. These patterns of movement can be determined through notational analysis of movement. The result is a stronger and faster athlete; a concept that is obviously beneficial in the explosive, sometimes collision-based, power-oriented world of sports, whatever sport or position you play.

So what do we mean by position-specific movement? This relates to two major concepts. Firstly, the nature of muscle action that can occur within sport-specific movements and secondly, the nature of joint actions that occur within sporting actions.

Muscular and Joint Action

There are three major types of muscular action that can be seen during sports performance, as outlined below. Refer to Chapter 2 for more information on muscle structure.

Concentric Action

This is where one or both myotendinous ends of the muscle (ie the tendon joining muscle to bone) move towards each other and the muscle is shortened, during the contraction.

Eccentric Action

This is where the muscle is actively lengthened while contracted. A muscle can only be lengthened by a greater opposing force, as it cannot actively lengthen by itself.

Isometric Action

Iso – same, *metric* – length. In this type of contraction the force generated by the muscle is equal to the resistive mass opposing it and so the muscle remains the same length while contracting.

Figure 22 illustrates the relationship between resistive load and muscular action in concentric, eccentric and isometric muscle action. 9.81 m/s^2 is the constant force exerted by gravity.

Concentric Action

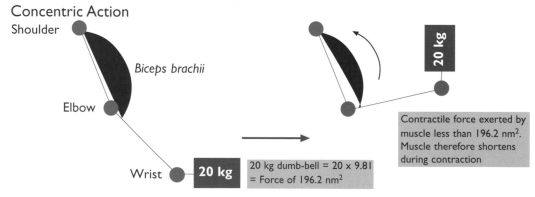

Eccentric Action

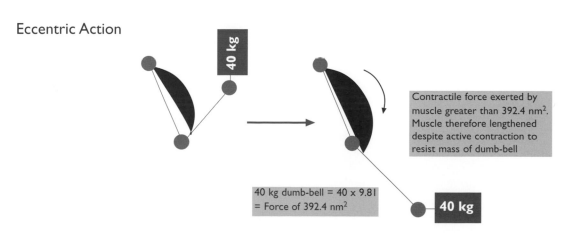

Figure 22: Resistive load and muscular action

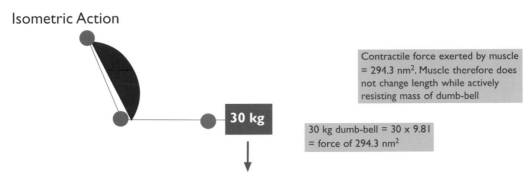

Isometric Action

Contractile force exerted by muscle = 294.3 nm². Muscle therefore does not change length while actively resisting mass of dumb-bell

30 kg

30 kg dumb-bell = 30 x 9.81 = force of 294.3 nm²

Figure 22: Resistive load and muscular action cont.

Stretch-shortening Action

As discussed in Chapter 2, the stretch-shortening cycle of muscular contraction involves stretch receptors in a muscle sensing the rate and length of the stretch in a fibre. These receptors initiate a forceful, reflex, concentric contraction in the muscle when the rate of strength reaches a threshold point. Many sporting actions rely on this to enable a muscle to reach maximal strength in a short space of time. This works by stretching a muscle and then relying on its elastic properties to produce greater forces than are normally possible in the reflex contraction (ie as the muscle returns to its resting length). In order to achieve this greater muscular force, the muscle must contract within the shortest possible time after it has been lengthened.

As identified in Chapter 2, muscles are either contracted or they are not. Those muscles that are responsible for the initiation of a particular movement are called *prime movers*. As we know, muscles are arranged in pairs and every muscle has an opposing muscle or group of muscles. While it is easy to think that when a muscle is active, its antagonistic/opposing partner is not, in reality this is very rarely the case. The opposing muscle is usually involved in a stabilising role or it is eccentrically working to brake or control the movement created in a joint by the prime mover. Thus muscles can be prime movers in one movement, stabilisers in another, and synergists (muscles that can indirectly assist the prime movers) in other movements. This is particularly important when a prime mover crosses two joints. A classic example can be seen in the deadlift in Figure 23 (a full breakdown of this lift can be seen in the following pages).

Figure 23: The deadlift

This exercise involves the simultaneous extension of the knee and hip joints from the starting position shown above. In order to achieve this, the *Quadriceps* muscle group is the prime mover. Of this group, the *Rectus femoris* muscle crosses both the hip and the knee joint, and is responsible for flexion in the hip and extension of the knee. If both of these actions were to occur simultaneously, the athlete performing the deadlift would not be able to stand straight up from the start position. Therefore, the *Gluteal* muscles in the buttock are also concentrically contracted at the same time as the *Rectus femoris*. Broadly speaking, in this activity, the *Gluteal* muscles are responsible for hip extension, and this action counters the hip-flexing actions of the *Rectus femoris* muscle. This then allows the hip and knee to extend and the athlete to perform the full deadlift, ending in a standing position.

Understanding the Nature of Movement-specific Strength Training for Sports

The importance of specificity of training has been highlighted in previous chapters when discussing the principles that underpin effective training. There are many books and training routines published that provide information for aspiring bodybuilders and fitness training participants. However, many of these are not suitable for the development of a games player, as the routines involved do not replicate the force production or movement demands of modern sport.

A strength-training programme needs to reflect the joint involvement and movement pattern, muscle actions and intensity of activity that are related to the particular sport for which the athlete is training. As such, effective strength training for sports performers begins with a working knowledge of basic movement mechanics. Kinesiological analysis[19] of any sporting movement will indicate that the basis of strength–power training exercises for an athlete in any sport should be closed-kinetic-chain exercises[20]. These exercises allow maximum force in gross-muscle structure (especially around the legs, hips and trunk) to be reached in minimum time. It is well documented that strength (the ability to produce force) and power (the product of force x velocity) gain is specific to the angle of the joint at which training occurs. The training actions and programme design should therefore reflect the total dynamic range of movement that an athlete might require in sports performance.

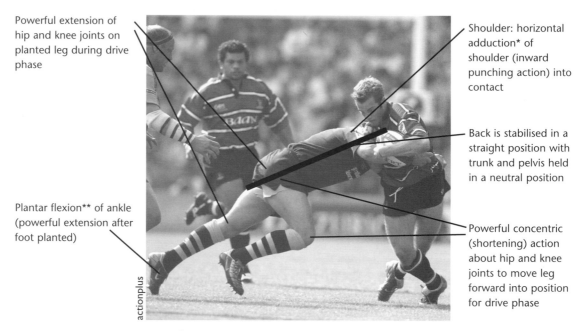

Powerful extension of hip and knee joints on planted leg during drive phase

Shoulder: horizontal adduction* of shoulder (inward punching action) into contact

Back is stabilised in a straight position with trunk and pelvis held in a neutral position

Plantar flexion** of ankle (powerful extension after foot planted)

Powerful concentric (shortening) action about hip and knee joints to move leg forward into position for drive phase

Figure 24: Basic kinesiological analysis of the head-on tackle in rugby union

*the movement of a muscle or limb towards the midline of the body
**the movement of pointing toes downwards by extension of the ankle
***the movement of a muscle or limb away from the midline of the body

(Hidden shoulder) horizontal adduction* of shoulder and powerful extension of elbow into the shot

Horizontal abduction*** (movement away from body) of shoulder and powerful extension of the elbow into the shot

Rotation of trunk about the hip joint

Powerful triple extension (ankle, knee, hip) as the player stands (from a flexed position) to catch the ball

Back is stabilised in straight position with trunk and pelvis held in a neutral position

Powerful triple extension (hip, knee, ankle) from flexed positions as the player moves into the shot

actionplus

Figure 25: Basic kinesiological analysis of the hook shot in cricket

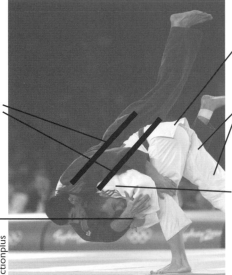

Rotation of trunk about the hip joint

Back is stabilised in a straight position with trunk and pelvis held in a neutral position

Sweeping leg: powerful triple extension of hip, knee and ankle

(Hidden shoulder) horizontal adduction* of shoulder into throw

Horizontal abduction*** of shoulder into throw

actionplus

Figure 26: Basic kinesiological analysis of a judo throw

Powerful extension of elbow into shot

Powerful shoulder flexion from the extended position

Powerful extension of hips, knees and ankles (plantar flexion) to generate vertical and rotational power to give height and speed to serve

Back is stabilised in a straight position with trunk and pelvis held in a neutral position. Very strong position from which to generate power in the limbs

Clive Brewer

Figure 27: Basic kinesiological analysis of a tennis serve

Figures 24–27 illustrate the actions of the joints as a function of the prime movers' actions. They do not indicate where, if at all, the joint actions are occurring as a result of gravity or momentum, nor do they indicate any synergistic or stabilising activity occurring in any of the muscles. The purpose of such basic analysis is to enable a coach of a particular sport to calculate the major joint movements involved in that sport and begin to replicate these actions in training movements.

Figures 28–30 show the movement patterns of three major weight-lifting movements (the techniques for which are found on the following pages). Comparison between the kinesiological demands of many primary sporting movements (ie Figures 24–27) and these training movements indicate many similarities in terms of:

• total body movements

• coordinated triple extensions of the ankle, knee and hip

• coordinated triple flexions of the ankle, knee and hip

• postural control in terms of maintaining a neutral position in the back, pelvic and shoulder girdles, from which to provide a power base for high-velocity limb movements.

Figure 28: The clean lifting technique

Figure 29: The snatch lifting technique

Figure 30: The squat lifting technique

These movement patterns are adaptable to encompass unilateral, rotational and multi-directional movements (ie single-leg lifts, unbalanced bars – more weight on one end than the other etc) in more competent athletes.

These kinesiological analyses provide further evidence for basing strength-training exercises for the games player on closed-kinetic-chain exercises (exercises where the body has a point in contact with the ground) that allow maximum force in gross muscle structure to be reached in minimum time. Similarly, when considering pre-habilitation of injuries, coaches need to ensure that the neuromuscular system is adequately trained to tolerate the strains imposed during functional tasks. Particular emphasis on trunk stability (sometimes referred to as *core stability*) has been a feature in contemporary sports medicine. This stems from the realisation that inappropriate muscular recruitment is the cause of a number of injuries in elite sportspersons, relating to the musculature of the lumbar spine, trunk and groin regions.

Weight Lifting

As sport is about moving the total body and involves few movements that isolate single joints, strength-training sessions should focus on multiple-joint lifts that stress the entire body, without focusing on individual body parts. Two to three sessions of such workouts per week also allow *every* body-part to receive two to three quality workouts per week rather than one. These lifts also facilitate the development of intra-muscular coordination, thus providing vital support for skill learning and performance that single-joint/isolated muscle-group lifts do not provide.

As mentioned earlier, strength gain is specific to the angle of the joint at which training occurs. Given this consideration and the nature of hip action and gross-muscle involvement required in games-based sports, exercises such as the squat, deadlift and derivatives of the clean, snatch and presses form the cornerstone of recommended resistance-training routines. Particular emphasis should be placed on the upward movements of these exercises as, for some sports such as sprinting, it is the vertical component of force that is the biggest predictor of speed and power.

These exercises also facilitate the incorporation of countermovements[21] in both slow (squat) and fast (squat clean, snatch, press and jerk) movements. They also dead-stop start accelerations (deadlifts, squat clean, snatch) that involve the overcoming of inertia in order to get a relatively large load moving from a static position and have been demonstrated as being maximally beneficial to sports performance and muscular growth.

Weight-lifting and Training Technique

It has already been demonstrated that there are many ways in which to use resistance training in order to achieve different objectives. It is important to understand that the lifts presented here may have different versions and uses, particular to an individual context. The exercises and coaching points presented are designed to communicate the most beneficial means of using particular techniques to develop strength/power for sportspeople. Some differences in terminology between disciplines are worth highlighting here. It is recognised that weightlifting (one word, a sport in its own right) and weight lifting (two words) for sports conditioning may be slightly different. The bodybuilding shrug and the power shrug used in sports training also differ.

The coaching/lifting method (explained below) for the weight-lifting movements is known as the *double-knee-bend* (DKB) technique. This has been demonstrated to be the most powerful method of completing lifts, such as the snatch and clean, and is certainly the most specific for sports training (Stone, 2005). The DKB allows a greater force to be transmitted more effectively and greater transfer of training effects to other sports, and it is also a safer lift with less potential risk to the back. This method ensures that the knees and hips are placed in the optimum position for generating vertical power, similar to that used in many sports movements. The DKB also ensures a plyometric (stretch-reflex) response can be induced in the thigh muscles, making for a highly effective and powerful training movement (Brewer et al, 2005).

The DKB must occur if the lift is to be optimal (Stone, 2005). It is the optimal technique to derive the benefits these lifts offer. Some coaches may say you cannot teach the DKB because it is stretch reflex. But why does this stretch reflex happen? Again, the first pull technique should be executed correctly, thus placing the athlete in the proper position to elicit the stretch-shortening cycle. This technique certainly can, and should, be coached (Brewer et al, 2005 and Stone, 2005). Waiting for the athlete to stumble upon the technique as an *accidental phenomenon* will only allow incorrect motor patterns to establish themselves. We are creatures of habit and, as such, proper technique should become a habit rather than an accidental phenomenon.

It is hard to imagine taking the same accidental approach when teaching a squat, where many athletes find a full range of movement difficult while keeping their heels on the floor. Do we just allow them to squat on their toes because they were unable to execute proper technique right away?

It is hard, in fact, to argue a case for any coach not wanting to develop correct technique in performers from the outset of learning a skill. It is most unlikely that an athlete will not be able to execute the correct weight-lifting technique after proper instruction. How quickly they learn the technique depends on the individual as well as on the experience and ability of the coach.

Using the Appropriate Equipment

The lifts in this section can all be done with either an Olympic barbell or a dumb-bell. Barbells are long bars that are held in two hands, dumb-bells are held in one hand. The use of barbells enables the player to move the maximum possible weight in total-body lifts and allows the double-knee bend to be performed. Using dumb-bells allows each side of the body to be moved independently, which means that left–right differences that may develop in sports performers (and which may be masked by barbell lifting) can be identified and trained. It is should be noted, however, that using a dumb-bell to perform many of these lifts is a relatively advanced concept. Therefore, a player is encouraged to learn the lifts with a barbell before performing them with a dumb-bell in an adapted movement.

The use of an Olympic barbell is important for most of the major weight-lifting exercises described. An Olympic barbell is one that has free-rotating ends (these come in a range of weights from 10–20 kilograms), whereas a normal barbell does not and is usually a lot lighter than an unloaded Olympic bar.

10 kg Olympic bar loaded with 2 x 5 kg discs

Unloaded 20 kg Olympic bar

'Normal' 8 kg barbell loaded with 2 x 6 kg discs

Figure 31: A range of bars all weighing 20 kg

When performing a lift such as the clean or the snatch (see following pages), angular momentum is created as the bar is accelerated upwards and the player rotates under the bar. With an Olympic bar, the bar will spin, while the discs and bar ends remain relatively still. In a normal bar, where the ends do not rotate, this angular momentum may cause the player's wrist to rotate excessively, causing injury to the joint structures.

You will notice, in the following figures, that the weight discs are not secured with collars on the bars. This allows the coach and player to receive immediate feedback about any left–right imbalances in the technique, as this may cause the disks to move.

The following exercise summaries are designed as a guide to the free-weight exercises that should form the cornerstone of any strength-/power-training schedules for any sport. As with any training technique, however, it is imperative that all players are sure to develop appropriate technique prior to commencing serious training. With the correct technique, there is no reason why any form of training should promote injury in a player.

The Major Lifts

Major conditioning lifts should form the cornerstone of any strength-/power-training programme for a sports performer. This section is followed by a supplementary exercises section: these exercises either allow the athlete to become stronger in ways that will enable them to perform the major conditioning lifts in a more powerful and efficient manner, or they may be beneficial to certain sports in aiding the performer to become stronger in specific positions/ranges of motion.

Between them, these major conditioning lift exercises, form the basis of a programme that will work every neuromuscular and joint complex in the body. The following exercise summaries are designed to provide a coach with basic guidelines and coaching tips to follow while carrying out these exercises. They are not a substitute for instruction by qualified and experienced strength and conditioning coaches[22].

Back Squat

You can do whatever you want to get a player strong as long as they are doing squats! The squat is considered an essential exercise in the stimulation of increased, overall strength, increased ligament and tendon strength, increased bone density, development of large musculature around the lower back, hip and knee, and improved neuromuscular efficiency that aids performance in biomechanically similar movements.

Setting the Bar (Figure 32)

- Place the bar in the squat rack/stand, at a level slightly below shoulder height. Always walk into the squat frame.

- Settle the bar across the base of the neck, so that it rests across the top of the *Deltoids* and *Trapezius* muscles. It is essential that you position yourself in the middle of the bar before any movement is attempted.

- Hold the bar in an overgrasp grip, with the hands evenly spaced, so that the elbows are bent to 90°.

- From this position, stand straight up and take 2–3 steps backwards.

Start (also Finish) Position

- Fix your eyes on a point in front of you, slightly above eye level, and keep your eyes focused on this point throughout the lift. This will keep the head up throughout the lift, which will in turn aid in keeping the back flat throughout the movement (Figure 33).

- The shoulders and chest are also important in keeping the back flat: you should pull the shoulder blades back fully (try to imagine that you have to hold a £5 note in between your shoulder blades) and at the same time push the chest upwards and outwards (Figure 32).

- Maintain the hand position as described earlier.

- Your feet should be flat on the floor, and shoulder-width apart (although those with long legs or poor flexibility may benefit from a wider stance). Most lifters find it more comfortable to have the toes pointing slightly outwards but, equally, they can face forward; it is a matter of individual style.

Figure 32: Addressing the bar in the squat rack

Figure 33: Start and finish position

Beginning the Descent

- Immediately before beginning the lift, you should take a deep breath in. This should be held until the very final stages of the lift. This will aid trunk stability by increasing intra-abdominal pressure.

- Prior to moving, you should actively tighten the lower back and the *Gluteal* muscles in the buttocks. This will enable the knees to move in the correct plane during the lift.

- Begin the movement by flexing the hips and the knees simultaneously. The trunk should be kept upright throughout the lift, with the back straight (in a neutral position, which means displaying a normal inward (lumbar lordotic) curve in the lumbar/lower spine).

- Knees should be moving along a line that points in the same direction as the toes (Figure 36). Common mistakes occur at this stage, with players bringing their knees inwards into very weak positions during the descent (*Bambi knees*).

- Continue the downward movement until the thighs break parallel with the floor. This means that the knees will bend past 90°. Despite popular beliefs to the contrary, this is fine in any athlete. Indeed, the knee is designed to go through a full range of movement, and will do so in most sporting situations. Therefore it is important they are trained in such positions.

Figure 34: The descent

Figure 35: The bottom position

The Bottom Position (Figure 35)

- The top of the thighs will have broken parallel at this point – you should go as low as possible while maintaining the correct technique. The feet should still be flat on the floor at all times throughout the lift. At this stage of the lift, the centre of pressure of the weight will be towards the rear of the mid-foot. Players with poor Achilles tendon flexibility will commonly not be able to get this full range of movement without the heels coming off the floor. This should be avoided at all costs, as it will cause the weighted bar to move forward, tipping the player off balance.

- The best way to improve the ankle's range of movement is to work through it, but remedial stretching will help. In the short term, having a wider stance may help, or in extreme cases, a small weights plate can be put under the heels of the player. However, the size of this plate should be progressively reduced over time to encourage the player to achieve the full range of movement. Weightlifting shoes, which have an inbuilt heel-raise (as worn by the athletes in the demonstrations) will help this.

- The trunk should still be upright, with the chest pushed upwards. Eyes should still be focused on the same point, and the shoulders should still be pulled back.

Figure 36: The bottom position

The Ascent

- The upward movement should be led by the chest, with the torso being kept upright. The hips and knees are extended by a powerful drive from the legs. Standing up should be an explosive action.

- Players whose legs are not strong enough at this stage will often seek to take the pressure off the legs by leaning the trunk forward, so the legs drive straight and the trunk comes forward. This means that the only part of the body left to lift the weight is the lower back, which is very vulnerable in this position. It is vital that the trunk remains in a stable, upright position.

- At the top of the lift, as you reach a standing position, you should exhale.

The Spotter

Most free-weight lifts do not need a spotter, but the squat is one that does. The role of the spotter is to aid the player should they get into any difficulty at some point during the lift (this may include aiding the lifter through a difficult/*sticking* point in the lift).

It is important that the spotter does not try to lift the bar. This can tip the player sideways or, more frequently, forwards and should be avoided. Communication problems between two spotters on either end of the bar can also have the same effect. The lifter needs to remain in control of the bar.

To spot the squat, the spotter should stay close to the lifter as they ascend and descend. If assistance is needed, the spotter should put their arms beneath the armpits of the lifter, so that the upper arm is resting under the armpit and then lift the lifter as the bar is moved upwards.

Figure 37: Spotting the squat

Front Squat

The front squat is an important lift for two reasons. Firstly, it is a progressive stage towards the squat clean; you cannot squat clean properly until you can front squat. Secondly, as an exercise in its own right, it moves the line of action of the mass of the bar away from the lower back (as in the back squat) to a position around the middle of the thighs (in front of the body). This takes the pressure off the lower back, but means that smaller muscles are utilised in the driving action, and so less weight can be lifted compared to the back squat.

Start (and Finish) Position

- You should ensure that you address the bar so that it is evenly balanced and that you are in the middle of the bar.

- The bar should be positioned so that it rests on the upper-front *Deltoids* and is held in place with an overgrasp clean grip with hands spaced approximately shoulder-width apart.

- Hold elbows high and level with the bar. This will require the wrists to be extended and the grip relaxed.

- As with the front squat, fix your eyes on a point slightly higher than eye level.

- The shoulder blades are pulled back (hold that £5 note!) and the chest is held high.

- The feet remain shoulder-width apart, pointing slightly outwards and remaining flat on the floor.

Figure 38: Front squat start (and finish) position

Figure 39: Front squat bottom position

The Lift

- The descent, bottom position and ascent of this lift are very similar to the back squat.

- Inhale prior to the start of the movement, with everything tightened, and the descent is from flexion of the hips and knees.

- The back must remain straight and upright throughout the lift, with the head up and shoulders back.

- The bottom position of the front squat is very similar, with the thighs breaking parallel and the knees pointing along the same line as the toes.

- Similarly, the ascent is led by the chest, with the knees and hips driving explosively upwards and the trunk remaining upright (with the natural lumbar lordotic curve).

Overhead Squat

This exercise is sometimes referred to as the *snatch squat*, as it is a vital component of the squat (full-range) snatch lift. Indeed, a games player cannot be expected to control a full snatch movement until they can perform the overhead squat lift.

This is one of the best exercises for developing trunk strength, as the player has to control the neutral pelvic position, the trunk position and the shoulder girdle throughout the full range of the dynamic movement. These demands make this an excellent conditioning movement for all sports.

The Start Position

- Hold the bar in a wide snatch grip (refer to Figure 45) above the head, with the elbows pointing along the length of the bar. The narrower the grip, the harder the exercise becomes.

- The arms should remain straight throughout the exercise.

- Raise the bar to a position that is above and slightly behind the head, with the arms staying extended throughout the lift.

- As with other squat movements, the head remains upwards throughout the lift, with the eyes focused on a point slightly above eye level.

- Follow the same trunk, chest and shoulder-blade positions as in the back squat.

The Bottom Position

- Descend until the thighs break parallel with the ground.

- The trunk should be upright, the head should remain up (eyes fixed on the same point as at the start of the lift), shoulder blades pulled back, chest high.

- The knees should still be pointing out along the same lines as the toes, and not be coming inwards.

The Ascent

As with all of the squatting movements, the upward drive should be controlled, explosive and led with the chest, so that the trunk remains upright throughout the movement.

Figure 40: Overhead squat start position

Figure 41: Overhead squat bottom position

The Snatch

The snatch lift is recognised as the most powerful whole-body human movement possible in sport. It is a multiple-joint lift that takes a bar from a static position (either on the floor or in a hang position, as demonstrated) to a position above the head.

The Grip

- Grip the bar with an overgrasp grip (hand comes over the top of the bar). The most secure method in which to grip the bar is to a use a hook grip, although this will initially feel uncomfortable when it is first used.

- To get the hook grip:
  - Place the flap of skin between the thumb and the index finger along the top of the bar. Position the thumb so that it is running along the length of the bar, pointing away from the body (Figure 42).
  - Close the remaining four fingers over the top of the bar and around it, so that the thumb is enclosed (as much as possible) by the fingers (Figure 43).

Figure 42: The hook grip stage 1

Figure 43: The hook grip stage 2

Determining Hand Spacing

The snatch lift uses a very wide hand spacing (relative to other lifts). In order to find out how wide the hands should be placed, follow the guidelines below:

- You should stand over the bar with the arms raised to a position parallel with the floor and fingertips touching each other (Figure 44).

- Some guides will tell you that the measurement from elbow to elbow in this position should be the width of the grip that you should use. If this is comfortable then you can use it.

- However, this is often too narrow for many people. Therefore, it is recommended that from the fingertips-touching position, the elbows are kept still and the arms moved outwards to grasp the bar. This will give you a more comfortable lifting grip width (Figure 45).

Figure 44: Elbow position

Figure 45: The snatch grip in the start position

The Start Position

- Start with the bar close to the shins.

- The feet go beneath the bar, which should be directly above the first hole (one nearest the shins) of the laces on the shoe.

- Bend the knees over the bar, with the hips slightly higher than the knees.

- Grip the bar in an overgrasp grip (hook grip recommended, but a claw grip – thumb around the bar – can be used if preferred).

- The arms should be straight, with the elbows locked outwards and pointing along the length of the bar.

- Hold the back straight (with a normal lordotic curve in the lumbar spine). This is aided by the shoulder blades being pulled back towards each other and the chest pushed out at the same time. Indeed, a coach standing in front of the player lifting should be able to see the whole of the chest from the front.

- The head should be up at all times.

- Immediately prior to the lift, inhale and pull all muscles tight, and take all of the slack out of the system (ie body plus bar). At the start of the lift, the centre of pressure of the bar is acting through the middle of the foot. This will move backwards as the bar begins to lift.

Figure 46: Snatch start position

First Pull
- Lift the bar from the floor slowly (see Figure 47). A common fault is to attempt to rip the bar straight from the floor, but the first stages of this lift are about overcoming inertia and giving the bar some momentum.

- The bar is moved by extending the knees (ie *knees back* position), but you should maintain the same angle between the back and the hips as there was at the start position. (A common mistake is to extend the knees, so that they extend fully, but also decrease the angle between the trunk and the hips, thus the bar is not raised vertically and the lower back becomes stressed.)

- Extend the knees until they are in a position that is slightly behind, and underneath, the bar. At this stage, the centre of pressure of the bar is towards the heel of the foot as it is planted on the floor (see Figure 48).

Figure 47: Snatch first movement

Figure 48: Snatch bar knee height

Transition Phase

- From the end of the first pull (bar at the top of the knees – see Figure 48), and without stopping the upward movement of the bar, you should now re-bend the knees and push them under and in front of the bar (Figure 49).

- At the same time, the trunk is brought into an upright position, with the bar moving to a position close to the waist at the upper-thigh level.

- The centre of pressure of the bar moves forward to the middle of the foot, in preparation for the following stage.

- The position of the body at this stage is similar to that which would be seen if the player were attempting a maximum vertical jump (Figure 50). This indicates the potential power that can be generated from this position.

- It is important that the arms stay straight at all times during this phase of the lift.

Figure 49: Mid-transition phase: knees moving under bar

Figure 50: Vertical jump position (side)

Figure 51: Vertical jump position (front)

The Jump and Second Pull

It is important to realise that the second pull progresses immediately from the first. They are distinct movements, but there is no time gap between them.

- As the bar reaches the top of the first pull and contacts the upper thigh, jump upwards.

- The ankles, knees and hips are powerfully and fully extended in sequence (the triple extension), which is followed by a violent shoulder shrug (see Figure 53). Although this is the realistic sequence that is followed in the lift (a progressive transfer of momentum), this stage is often coached as the shrug initiating the extension phase. This is because, in reality, there is little difference in timing between the joint extensions and the shrug, and players find it easier to think of initiating the movement with the shrug than following the extension with the shrug.

- At the start of the shrug, the centre of mass of the bar is towards the balls of the feet as you powerfully extend the ankle. It may be that you are able to generate sufficient power to get your feet to leave the ground completely, which is perfectly acceptable.

- This sequence of actions is completed with the arms straight and the wrists slightly flexed. Wrist flexion, combined with an aggressive shrug, will help to keep the bar very close to the trunk as it is raised. It is important to realise that, if the bar comes away from the trunk, it will start to pull the player forward at the upper stages of this lift.

- The second pull stage is completed with the arms straight, the elbows still pointing along the length of the bar.

There is a simple mantra that can be repeated by the player to aid performance of the lift and sequence the stages appropriately:

Start position -> knees back -> knees forward -> shrug and jump

Figure 52: Shrug and jump (front view) Figure 53: Shrug and jump (side view)

Figure 54: Dropping under the bar

The Catch

- At the top of the second pull, before the upward momentum of the bar is lost, your body has to drop below the bar (Figure 54). This is achieved by slightly flexing the elbows along the length of the bar (the bar should not move away from its position close to the body) and simultaneously dropping the body quickly under the bar. It is almost as if the bar is the pivot point about which the body is rotated as it moves under the bar.

- As the body rotates under the bar, the arms forcibly re-extend, pushing the bar upwards towards the ceiling (as if the bar was being thrown vertically in the air).

- As you come underneath the bar you will land on your heels, as the bar is caught at the bottom position of the overhead squat, with your arms fully extended (Figure 55).

If you are performing a *power snatch*, then the bar will be caught in a higher position, where the thighs have not lowered past a point of being parallel with the floor (Figure 56). This exercise requires the bar to be thrown higher in the air, but does not require the same amount of flexibility, speed and eccentric control (all of which are important qualities for the sportsperson to develop) as the *squat snatch*.

- From the bottom position, you should powerfully drive upwards into a standing position. The upward drive should be controlled, explosive and led with the chest, so that the trunk remains upright throughout the movement.

Figure 55: Squat snatch catch position

Figure 56: Power snatch catch position

Figure 57: The snatch finish position

Snatch from Hang Position

- A lift from the hang position is one that does not begin from the floor, but from either the knees (low hang) or the power position at the end of the first pull (high hang).

- From these start positions, complete the lifts as described above.

- These lifts do not develop the performer through the full range of motion, but they are a stage in the learning process and help to develop high levels of power through a limited range of movement.

Figure 58: Snatch from high hang position

High Pull: Snatch Grip

- The high pull involves completing the first and second pull stages of the snatch, finishing with the arms straight and the elbows still pointing along the length of the bar.

- The catch is not part of this lift, the bar is simply returned to the floor.

- This exercise allows you to focus on the stages of the lift associated with the development of vertical power.

Figure 59: High pull (snatch grip) end position

The Clean

The clean is a multiple-joint lift that takes a bar from a static position (either on the floor or in a hang position, as demonstrated in Figure 70) to a standing position on the front of the shoulders. The clean is also often used as part of a sequence of exercises in both a conditioning and a sport-specific sense (eg the recognised Olympic discipline of the clean and jerk).

The Grip

- Place your hands slightly wider than shoulder-width apart.

- Grasp the bar with an overgrasp grip (hand comes over the top of the bar).

- The most secure method in which to grip the bar is to a use a hook grip (see instructions in the snatch), although a claw grip (normal grip with the thumb around the bar) can also be used if this is perceived to be more comfortable.

The Start Position

- This is very similar to the snatch start, the major difference being the narrower hand position, which also allows the hips to be in slightly higher position at the start.

- Start with the bar close to the shins.

- The feet go beneath the bar, which should be directly above the first hole (one nearest the shins) of the laces on the shoe.

- The knees are bent over the bar, with the hips slightly higher than the knees.

- The arms should be straight, with the elbows locked outwards and pointing along the length of the bar.

- The back should be held straight (with a normal lordotic curve in the lumber spine). This is aided by the shoulder blades being pulled back towards each other and the chest pushed out at the same time.

- The head should also be up at all times.

- Immediately before the lift, you should inhale, pull all muscles tight and take all of the slack out of the system. At the start of the lift, the centre of pressure of the bar is acting through the middle of the foot. This will move backwards as the bar begins to lift.

Figure 60: Clean start position

First Pull

- As with the snatch, in order to overcome the inertia of the static bar on the floor, the initial movements of the lift are relatively slow.

- The bar is moved by extending the knees (ie *knees back*), but you should maintain the same angle between the back and the hips as there was at the start position. It is crucial that this angle is maintained as the bar is lifted, to avoid putting pressure on the lumbar spine or pulling you forward.

- At all times in this lift, the bar should travel right up the front of the body and never be more than an inch away from you, otherwise you will be pulled forward, off balance.

- The knees are extended until they are in a position that is slightly behind, and underneath, the bar (Figures 61 and 62). At this stage, the centre of pressure of the bar should be acting towards the heel of the foot, which remains planted on the floor.

Figure 61: End of first pull bar at the knees

Figure 62: End of first pull

Transition Phase

- From this position (knees slightly under the bar), and without stopping the upward movement of the bar, you should now re-bend the knees and push them under and in front of the bar.

- At the same time, the trunk is brought into an upright position, with the bar moving to a position close to the waist at the mid-thigh level (with the hands closer together, the bar will not raise as high as in the snatch lift).

- The centre of pressure of the bar moves forward to the middle of the foot, in preparation for the following stage.

- The position of the body at this stage is similar to that which would be seen if you were attempting a maximum vertical jump (Figure 63). This indicates the potential power that can be generated from this position.

- It is important that the arms stay straight at all times during this phase of the lift.

Figure 63: The jump position – at the end of the transition phase

Jumping and the Second Pull

It is important to realise that the second pull progresses immediately from the first. They are distinct movements, but there is no time gap between them.

- As the bar reaches the top of the first pull and contacts the upper-mid thigh, jump upwards: the ankles, knees and hips are powerfully and fully extended in sequence (the triple extension), initiated by a violent shoulder shrug.

- At the start of the shrug, the centre of mass of the bar is towards the ball of the feet as you powerfully extend the ankle. It may be that you are able to generate sufficient power to get your feet to leave the ground completely, which is perfectly acceptable.

- This sequence of actions is completed with the arms straight and the wrists slightly flexed. Wrist flexion, combined with an aggressive shrug, will help to keep the bar very close to the trunk as it is raised. Remember, if the bar comes away from the trunk, it will start to pull you forward at the upper stages of this lift.

- The second pull stage is completed with the arms straight, the elbows still pointing along the length of the bar (Figure 64).

Figure 64: Clean just after start of second-pull triple extension

Figure 65: Rotate the wrists and elbows then jump under the bar

The Catch

- At the top of the second pull, after the completion of the full extension phase and before the upward momentum of the bar is lost, flex at the elbows, which are pointing along the length of the bar (the bar should not move away from its position close to the body), then rotate the wrists and elbows around to a position in front of the bar (Figure 65).

- At the same time as this is occurring, jump down under the bar, landing on flat feet with your weight resting on your heels, and catch the bar on the upper part of the *Deltoids*.

- In effect, the bar is caught at the bottom position of the front squat, with the elbows high in front of the bar (Figure 66).

- If you are performing a *power clean*, then the bar will be caught in a higher position, where the top of the thigh has not lowered past a point of being parallel with the floor (Figure 67). This exercise requires the bar to be thrown higher in the air, but does not require the same amount of flexibility, speed and eccentric control as the squat clean.

- From the bottom (catch) position, you should powerfully drive upwards into a standing position. The upward drive should be controlled, explosive and led with the chest, so that the trunk remains upright throughout the movement.

Figure 66: Catch position squat clean

Figure 67: Catch position power clean

Figure 68: Clean finish position

Clean from Hang Position
- A lift from the hang position is one that does not begin from the floor, but from either the knees (low hang in Figure 69) or the power position at the end of the first pull (high hang).

- From these start positions, complete the lifts as described above.

- These lifts do not develop the performer through the full range of motion, but they do represent a stage in learning the full lift and help to develop high levels of power through a limited range of movement.

- For most sports training, the squat clean is recommended as the core version that is used, as the greater range of motion required promotes greater speed, greater eccentric strength development and greater flexibility in a performer than a power clean.

High Pull: Clean Grip
- The high pull involves completing the first- and second-pull stages of the clean, finishing with the arms bending after the shrug has been completed and the elbows still pointing along the length of the bar (Figure 70).

- The catch is not part of this lift; the bar is simply returned to the floor. This exercise allows the player to focus on the stages of the lift associated with the development of vertical power.

Figure 69: Clean from low hang position

Figure 70: High pull

Split Snatch and Split Clean
The split snatch and split clean involve the same basic lifting principles and technique as the normal (squat or power) snatch and clean. The difference between the two lifts occurs after the first pull. The aim of this lift is to land with the legs split evenly, forming a stable base, rather than landing with legs together. This helps to develop unilateral, eccentric strength and dynamic balance in muscles, as well as leg-drive to the standing position from the legs in a split position. Such unilateral positions are very relevant to many sports. However, the range of movement in this lift is less in the ankles, knees, hips and lower

back than in the squat clean or snatch, and also requires less flexibility in the shoulders when compared to the squat snatch. Therefore, it is not recommended that this type of lift is performed exclusively in a programme, in preference to the squat clean or snatch.

The Lift

- From the power position, perform the same explosive upwards jumping movement as in the squat clean/snatch, through the second-pull stages of the lift. The ankles, knees and hips are powerfully and fully extended in sequence (the triple extension), which is initiated by a violent shoulder shrug (see Figure 74).

- This sequence of actions is completed with the arms straight and the wrists slightly flexed. Wrist flexion, combined with an aggressive shrug, will help to keep the bar very close to the trunk as it is raised. Remember, if the bar comes away from the trunk, it will start to pull you forward at the upper stages of this lift.

- The arm action for the catch sequence of the lift should follow that of the snatch/clean, as appropriate, at the end of the second-pull phase.

- At the top of the full extension of the ankles, knees and hips, you should split the legs. This should be done about an imaginary cross, known as a Murray Cross, which can be drawn on the lifting platform if it helps (see Figure 71).

- The front leg (this should be alternated with each repetition) should be planted flat on the floor (centre of pressure should be on the heel of this foot) at 45° to the centre of the cross (so the foot has moved forwards and sideways).

- Your centre of mass should be immediately above the centre of the cross (see Figures 72, 73 and 75).

- Simultaneously, the back foot moves backwards, again at a 45° angle to the centre of the cross. You should land on the ball of the foot.

- After the split position has been achieved and once stabilised, the feet should be moved back to a position shoulder-width apart. This should start with the front foot moving backwards towards the mid-line, then the rear foot moving forwards.

- The lift is completed with both feet level and the bar either at the shoulder (clean) or fully extended overhead (snatch).

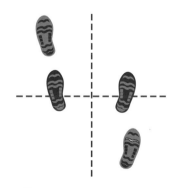

This illustrates the movement of the foot from the start position (dark blue) of the lift to the split position (light blue).
(Remember, this should be reversed on alternate lifts, so the player leads with the right leg on the next lift).

Figure 71: The Murray Cross

Figure 72: Split snatch catch (side view)

Figure 73: Split snatch catch (front view)

Figure 74: Split clean end of pull phase

Figure 75: Split clean catch

The Deadlift

The deadlift is one of the major mass-and-strength-developing exercises for the legs and back. It is a pulling movement that involves taking a heavy weight from a static position on the floor, to a position near the mid-thigh, when standing. Although this lift forms part of the sport of power lifting, the speed component of this lift is normally minimal and it is therefore regarded as a maximal strength, rather than a power, exercise.

Start Position

- The start position is very similar to the power clean.

- Assume a stance with feet shoulder-width apart and flat on the floor.

- The bar should be close to the shins, over the balls of the feet (over the first or second eye of the shoelaces).

- Squat down so that the knees come in front of the bar, pointing along the line of the toes, with the hips slightly above the level of the knee (Figure 77).

- Either a closed, overgrasp grip, or an alternate grip (one hand over the bar, one hand under the bar – Figure 76) should be used (whichever is comfortable for the individual).

- Your hands should be positioned slightly wider than shoulder-width apart.

- The elbows should be fully extended, and remain so throughout the lift.

- Your shoulders should be positioned so that they are 4–5 cms in front of the bar, with the shoulder blades pulled back and together and the chest pushed up.

- The head should be up and looking slightly upwards.

Figure 76: Deadlift start position

The Lift

- Immediately prior to moving, inhale and pull everything tight.

- The lift is executed by the simultaneous extension of the hips and knees to set the bar in motion (see Figure 77).

- The initial movement of the bar takes it back towards the shins, after which it is lifted straight up the front of the legs as they straighten.

- The hips are driven forward and knees pulled back at the same rate, with the trunk–thigh angle increasing at a constant rate.

- The bar is kept close to the body, with elbows fully extended, head looking slightly upwards and shoulders positioned slightly over the bar until the final stages of the lift.

- You should continue until the knees and hips are fully extended, establishing an erect body position to complete the lift.

Figure 77: Deadlift transition   **Figure 78: Deadlift finish position**

Stiff-leg Deadlift

This is a crucial lift for sports performers for two main reasons; firstly, as an assistance exercise for developing clean and snatch technique and secondly, as a means of developing eccentric strength in the *Hamstring* muscles. This is something that is often poorly developed in many sports training programmes. Indeed, despite the fact that the many hamstring injuries occur during eccentric contractions or extended positions, most hamstring strength work has traditionally focused on concentric training motions.

Start Position

- Hold the bar in an overgrasp grip (hook or claw, according to your preference).

- The hands should be shoulder-width apart, with the elbows straight unless you are using this to develop snatch technique, in which case a snatch grip can be used (Figure 79).

- The trunk should be erect, the head up, the shoulder blades pulled back and the chest up.

- The knees should be slightly bent (this is not, as commonly thought, a straight-leg deadlift). This knee position is crucial and, once the bent-knee position has been established, it should not be adjusted at all during the movement of the lift.

Figure 79: Stiff-leg deadlift (start position) with snatch grip

The Descent
- Maintaining the straight back (with the shoulders pulled back) and knee position, the bar is lowered, under control, directly down the front of the thighs.

- This movement is aided by flexing the hips (not the knees) as the bar gets lower.

- It is important to maintain a straight back (with the normal slight inward curve in a the lower spine) throughout the movement.

- The descent continues until the *Hamstrings* become fully stretched and tight.

The Ascent
- From the bottom position (full stretch on the *Hamstrings*), the trunk is returned to the start position through hip extension and raising the trunk.

- The bar should return along the same path as it descended until you have returned to the start position.

Figure 80: Stiff-leg deadlift (bottom position) with clean grip

Push Press

This is an overhead lift that involves the player moving the bar from the shoulders to a finishing point with the bar straight above head, arms locked out. However, the majority of the power in allowing this movement comes from the triple extension of the hips, knees and ankles, with minimal upper body (shoulder and arm extension) work at the end of the lift. This sequential transfer of power makes the lift specific to many sports.

Start Position
- The start position for this lift is the same as the end position for the power clean and front squat (see Figure 81).

- The bar rests across the *Anterior deltoids,* held in an overgrasp grip.

- The elbows should be pointing forward.

- The head should be up, shoulder blades pulled back and trunk straight.

- The feet should be shoulder-width apart.

Figure 81: Push press start position

Alternative Start Position

- This lift can be started with the bar behind your head, resting across the top of the *Deltoids* (the start position for the back squat).

- This changes the line of action of the mass of the bar from the front of the body to the rear.

Figure 82: Push press alternative start position

The Descent

- Prior to any movement, pull everything tight.

- Bend the knees to an angle of 135–45° (Figure 83). This is the position that a player would intuitively adopt if undertaking an explosive vertical jump; it is the optimum angle for generating vertical power.

- At the same time, the elbows can be dropped below the bar, so that they are pointing straight down at the ground.

Figure 83: Push press bottom of descent

The Ascent

- Having dropped the elbows and bent the knees to the bottom position, inhale and then carry out an immediate explosive upward extension of the knees and hips, coordinated with a simultaneous extension of the arms, as the bar is *thrown* directly upwards.

- This extension is full and the lift is completed with the arms locked out overhead and the feet flat on the floor.

- Exhale as the bar reaches its top position.

- From here, the bar is lowered slowly to the start position.

Figure 84: Push press finish position

The Push Jerk

The push jerk involves a similar movement to the push press, but the jerk involves a countermovement to come underneath and catch the rising bar.

Start Position
The start position for this lift is the same as the push press (see Figure 81).

The Descent
- Prior to any movement, pull everything tight.

- The knees are now bent to an angle of 135–45°.

- At the same time, the elbows can be rotated around the bar, so they are pointing straight down at the ground (Figure 83).

The Ascent
- The hips, knees and ankles extend explosively to send the bar upwards.

- As this occurs, drop under the bar by re-bending the hips and knees (trunk remains upright) and catch the bar in an overhead position with the elbows fully extended (Figure 85).

- The centre of mass is acting through the heels at the bottom of the squat.

Figure 85: Push jerk catch position

Finish Position

• Maintaining the fully extended arm position, complete the lift by fully extending the hips and knees.

Figure 86: Push jerk finish position

The Split Jerk

This lift combines the explosive extension and countermovement actions of the jerk with the unilateral leg movements of the split clean/snatch.

Start Position

Both the start and alternative start positions for this lift are the same as for the push press.

The Descent

• Prior to moving, inhale and pull everything tight.

• The first movement is an explosive drop into a quarter-squat position under the bar, with the centre of pressure towards the middle of the foot. See Figure 83.

The Split Lift

• From the bottom of the quarter-squat position, you simultaneously split the legs (into the same pattern as demonstrated in the split clean/snatch) and extend the elbows.

• You will therefore finish in the lunge position with the bar extended fully over head (Figure 87).

• The front foot should land flat on the ground, with the rear foot landing on the ball of the foot.

• Your centre of mass should be over the middle of the imaginary Murray Cross (see Figure 71, page 67). This puts you in a well-balanced position (Figure 88).

• From the catch position, move the front foot backwards, then the back foot forwards, until the feet are level.

• The bar is still extended in the overhead position when the lift is completed.

Figure 87: Split jerk catch position (front view)

Figure 88: Split jerk catch position (side view)

Supplementary Exercises

The following exercises are multiple-joint exercises that coaches may find useful to include in a training programme in addition to the core lifts, as required by the specific demands of the sport.

The Power Shrug

The shrug element of the clean and snatch lifts is often the weakest part of the lift in many performers. The ability to explosively shrug the shoulders is vital in helping the bar move upwards along the front of the trunk. The shrug also forms the basis of many sport-specific movements and skills. This lift is different from the traditional bodybuilding shrug, which is a slow movement designed to develop the *Trapezius* muscle.

Figure 89: Power shrug start (snatch) position (clean grip)

Figure 90: Power shrug top position (snatch grip)

- This lift can be performed with either a clean (close) or snatch (wide) grip.
- You begin in the power position for either the clean (with bar mid-thigh) or the snatch (with bar against upper thigh) as demonstrated in Figure 89.
- The wrists should be slightly flexed (to help the bar move upwards in front of the body) rather than out and away from the body.
- The elbows should be fully extended and point along the line of the bar.
- This arm position should be maintained throughout the lift.
- From here, the shoulders should be explosively raised straight up towards the ears. A common mistake is to bring the neck down, so that the ears meet the shoulders; this should be avoided, ensuring the shoulders are always raised instead.
- It may be possible to generate enough power from this movement to force the hips, knees and ankles to extend (triple extension) – see Figure 90. This should always be the aim because, as previously discussed, the shrug effectively initiates the triple extension and jumping action during the clean/snatch lifts.
- The arms stay straight throughout the movement (Figure 90).
- The lift is completed by the bar returning (under control) to the start position.

Bench Press

- This lift works the *Pectorals* in the chest in a horizontal abduction motion, and the *Triceps* (elbow extensors).
- Lie flat on the bench, with knees bent and feet flat on the floor.
- The buttocks and shoulder blades should be kept in contact with the bench while the back is flat and the chest is expanded.
- Hold the bar with a medium (overgrasp) grip, with the bar directly above the chest (Figure 91).
- Inhale and pull everything tight prior to lifting, then lower the bar directly to the chest, slightly lower than nipple level (Figure 92).
- When pressing to the starting position, the bar is pressed upwards and slightly back towards the shoulders ('J' lift).

• A spotter is important in bench-press exercises (see Figure 93) to ensure the weight can be lifted off the player's chest should they get into any difficulty.

Figure 91: Bench press start position

Figure 92: Bench press bottom position

Close-grip Bench Press

This is an adaptation of the bench press outlined above. In order to put more emphasis on the arm extension (*Tricep*) component of the exercise, the grip can be narrowed, to anything from shoulder-width to 10 centimetres apart. As the bar is lowered, you must ensure that you keep the elbows pointing forwards.

Figure 93: Close-grip bench press bottom position, with spotter

Single Leg Squat or Lunge

This is one of the most versatile exercises and, with some imagination from the coach, the potential sport-specific variations of the central principles are numerous.

Start position
• The start position for this lift is the same as for the push press, with the bar being held either behind the head (squat grip) or in front of the head (held as if for the front squat).
• The head is up, the shoulder blades are pulled back together and the chest is out (Figure 94).

Figure 94: Single-leg squat start position (bar in front)

The Lift

• Prior to making the first movement, inhale and tighten the trunk/gluteal musculature.

• From here, you deliberately flex the hip of the leg that will be leading the movement (refer to Figure 95). The knee of this leg should also be flexed, both to an angle of 90°. You should alternate the lead leg in order to ensure balanced development.

• Now take an exaggerated step forwards with the lead leg, which is planted flat on the ground.

• Flex the lead knee, so that it is moving along the same line of direction as the toes of the lead foot (refer to Figure 96).

• At the same time, come onto the ball of the foot on the trail leg and lower the knee of this leg to a bottom position that is approximately 3–5 cms off the floor.

• The trunk should be kept upright throughout the movement, with your centre of mass being directly above the mid-point between the two legs.

• To return to the starting position, push back forcefully with the lead leg so that the starting position is returned to. Repeat with the other leg for the next repetition.

Figure 95: Single-leg squat first movement (bar in front) **Figure 96: Single-leg squat bottom position (bar in front)** **Figure 97: Single-leg squat bottom position (bar extended above the head)**

Alternative Single-leg Squats

This lift can also be performed with a pressing action, by forcefully extending the arms above the head, as the step with the lead leg is taken. This means that as the front foot lands, the arms are fully extended, with the bar directly above the head. The trunk remains upright throughout (see Figure 97).

Figure 98: Single-leg squat (bar behind neck)

The exercise described above is linear in nature, in that the front foot moves forwards. However, as sport is multi-directional, this conditioning lift can be manipulated to allow the player to train for this. As long as the player follows the principles relating to the major steps of the lift[23], the lift can be adapted so that the front foot placement is open (to the side away from the body as demonstrated in Figure 99), closed (to the side across the body, as demonstrated in Figure 100) or even behind the player (as demonstrated in Figure 101). This can be done with the bar at the shoulders, or with a pressing/arm-extension action, or random combinations of all of the above.

A bench can also be used in single-leg squats. This makes the action less dynamic but it does tend to put more emphasis on controlling the balance and positioning of the lead knee in relation to the front (Figure 102). Similarly, the single-leg Cossack squat is an advanced exercise that really challenges dynamic balance as well as single-leg strength. These can be performed from a bench, either with or without dumb-bells (Figure 103).

Figure 99: Single-leg squat mid-point lunge with open step

Figure 100: Single-leg squat mid-point lunge and press with closed step

Figure 101: Single-leg squat mid-point lunge (bar behind neck) backward step

Figure 102: Single-leg squat (mid position)

Figure 103: Single-leg Cossack squats from bench (bottom position)

Bent-over Row

- You can perform this exercise with either a closed undergrasp grip, or an overgrasp claw grip, depending on which might be more appropriate for your sport.
- The hands should be held slightly wider than shoulder-width apart.
- Use the floor-to-thigh lifting technique, as described in the power clean.
- Assume a shoulder-width stance, with feet shoulder-width apart and knees slightly flexed.
- Lean torso forward to 10–30° above horizontal (see Figure 104) and look ahead/slightly upwards.

- The chest should be high, shoulder blades pulled back together and back normally straight.
- The lift begins with the elbows fully extended (the bar should not touch the floor).
- From here, tighten the musculature and inhale, then pull the bar into the trunk (see Figure 105), pointing elbows upwards during the movement.
- Maintain knee, head and torso position, and keep the back flat at all times.
- Return the bar to the starting position to complete the lift.

Figure 104: Bent-over row start position

Figure 105: Bent-over row top position

Dumb-bell Curl and Press

- Stand with dumb-bells in each hand, holding them with an undergrasp grip, sideways on, with palms facing forward.
- Your feet should be shoulder-width apart, flat on the floor with legs slightly bent.
- The head should be up, shoulder blades pulled back together and the chest up (see Figure 106).

Movement 1: Curl

- Keeping the elbows next to the body, the elbows are flexed and the dumb-bells are raised to shoulder level (see Figure 107).

Figure 106: Curl start position

Figure 107: End of curl

Movement 2: Press

- Once the dumb-bells are at shoulder level, rotate the wrists so that the palms are again facing forward.
- From here, extend the elbows vertically, so that the dumb-bells are raised to full arm extension (see Figure 109).
- At the end of this movement, the dumb-bells are returned to the start position.

Figure 108: Beginning the press **Figure 109: End of the press**

Alternative Dumb-bell Curl and Press Combination

This exercise is another that is very versatile, as the curl can be combined with a single-leg squat movement in the legs, or the press turned into a push jerk or split jerk.

Shoulder Press

This is the same movement as the push press, but the power to move the bar comes from the *Deltoids* in the shoulder and *Triceps* in the arm, rather than transferring power from the leg drive. In this way, the legs stay still throughout the movement.

Figure 110: Shoulder press start position **Figure 111: Shoulder press top position**

Alternative Shoulder Press

One suggested variation of this lift is to raise the bar from the front, lower it behind the head, and then push it from behind the head, lowering to the front.

Figure 112: Shoulder press (from behind the neck) start position

Dumb-bell Flies

This is another exercise that works the *Pectorals* in the chest in a horizontal adduction (inward punching/hugging action) movement of the shoulder.

- Lie face up on a bench, feet flat on the floor.
- Hold the dumb-bells with a closed, overgrasp grip, with the dumb-bells facing each other.
- To get into the correct start position, press the dumb-bells to an extended arm position above the chest, with the palms of the hands facing inwards (see Figure 113).
- From here, the elbow is slightly bent (to an angle that will remain constant from here) and then the dumb-bells are lowered, under control, in a wide arc, until the dumb-bell is at the same height as the shoulder (Figure 114).
- Both arms should lower (and later raise) at the same rate.
- Once the dumb-bells are in the bottom position, return them to the starting position. This is done by using the *Pectoral* (chest) muscles to pull the dumb-bells towards each other (keeping the angle of elbow flexion constant) to make the arms return to the start position.

Figure 113: Dumb-bell flies start position

Figure 114: Dumb-bell flies bottom position

Upright Row

This exercise strengthens the muscles around the neck, upper back and shoulder girdle, and strengthens in an upward pulling motion. The action is very similar in nature to the high-pull exercise. The major difference is that movement in this lift is initiated by flexion of the arms, rather than explosive extension of the hips and knees.

- Stand with the head up, shoulder blades back, chest high and feet flat on the floor, shoulder-width apart.
- Hold the bar in an overgrasp grip, with arms fully extended.
- Prior to any movement being made, inhale and pull the trunk and *Gluteal* muscles tight (Figure 115).
- From here, the elbows are flexed, pulling the bar up the front of the trunk until it reaches a position level with the top of the chest.
- The elbow should be above the level of the bar at all times (Figure 116) .
- From this position, the bar is lowered, under control, to the start position.

Figure 115: Upright row start position

Figure 116: Upright row top position

Triceps Dip

This is an excellent conditioning exercise for the *Triceps* muscles (responsible for straightening the arm) and it can also be adapted to train the chest as well. This exercise uses your own body weight to provide resistance, although when you can cope with this for the required number of repetitions, additional weight can be added to a belt around the waist, so that you are continually overloaded to stimulate development.

- Using a dip bar (or gymnastics parallel bar, depending upon equipment availability), hang from the rails with straight arms, leaning slightly forward (see Figure 117). The further the lean, the more the chest muscles become involved in the action.

- From here, lower the body, under control, until the elbows are bent to a 90° angle (see Figure 118).

- The elbows are then straightened and the body driven upwards, as rapidly as possible, until you return to the start position.

Figure 117: Tricep dip start position

Figure 118: Tricep dip bottom position

Pull-ups (Chin-ups)

This is another exercise that develops strength through lifting your own body weight (until such a time as additional weight needs to be added to facilitate overload). This exercise can be performed with an undergrasp grip or an overgrasp grip (see Figure 119), or it can be made more sport specific. For example, the judo player performing the exercise could grip a judo 'Gi' draped over the chin-up bar and a rugby player could grip a rugby shirt or simply a piece of rope.

- Begin by hanging from the bar, with arms fully extended (see Figure 119).

- From here, pull yourself up, so that the chin comes level with the bar (Figure 120), then return under control to the start position.

Some might argue that this action should occur with the body in a straight position. However, sport is about generating power through total body movement, and if the player finds it beneficial to use the lower body to generate the momentum required for the movement, then this is acceptable. Similarly, if the full range of movement cannot be achieved, then the player should be encouraged to perform as complete a range of motion as possible, particularly if grip strength is important to the sport for which they are training.

Figure 119: Pull-up start position (overgrasp grip)

Figure 120: Pull-up top position

Trunk-conditioning Exercises

Crunches

Crunches are considered to be the easiest of the trunk-conditioning exercises to perform.

- Lie on the floor, with your knees bent to 90° and feet flat on the floor.

- The hands should be folded across the chest (easiest method) or holding onto the ears but do not put them behind the neck (see Figure 121).

- The chin should be tucked onto the chest.

- From here, curl the trunk towards the legs until the upper back is off the mat, keeping the lower back and feet on the floor (see Figure 122).

- It is important not to bounce from the shoulders.

- Hold then slowly lower your trunk under control, keeping your chin tucked into your chest.

Figure 121: Crunch start position

Figure 122: Crunch top position

Cycled Crunches

- Lie on your back on the floor, with the hands holding on to the ears and elbows pointing towards the feet.

- Raise the feet and legs off the floor together, with a slight bend in the knees (this takes the pressure off the lower back).

- From here, the left leg is bent, with the knee moving up towards the head.

- Simultaneously, the trunk is flexed and rotated about a stable pelvis, which remains in a neutral position, while the lower back remains flat on the floor.

- The left elbow is brought to meet the right knee (see Figure 123).

- Relax and return to the start position, before repeating the action with the opposite arm and leg.

Figure 123: Cycled crunches

Vertical Leg Shoots

- Lie on the floor, with the hips bent to 90º, knees extended so that the feet are pointing straight up in the air, with the hands folded across the chest.
- Keeping this angle at the knee joint, use the lower abdominal muscles to tilt the pelvis back towards the head, so that the angle of the hip is increased and the feet are thrown up towards the sky (see Figure 124).
- Briefly hold this position and then return to the starting position, under control.
- This action is repeated, but it is important that the flexion/extension action of the hips between repetitions does not cause the legs to lower and rise. This would cause momentum to be generated, which makes the movement a lot easier.

Figure 124: Vertical leg shoots

V-sits

- Lie on your back on the floor, with the arms extended fully behind the head with hands pointing away from the body and the feet and legs raised off the floor together (see Figure 125).
- There should be a slight bend in the knees to take the pressure off the lower back.
- From here, maintaining a neutral pelvis position, perform a *jack-knife* manoeuvre, flexing the trunk and bringing the thighs towards the trunk (as if the upper and lower body segments were coming to meet each other at an imaginary line coming up from the hip joint in the start position).
- The legs should remain stiff with knees slightly bent, at the same angle throughout the movement.
- Extend the arms above the head until the trunk has reached full flexion, at which point bring them forward to meet the feet, as the 'V' position is achieved.

Figure 125: V-sits top position

Windscreen Wipers

Lie flat on the back, hips flexed at 90º and legs straight, with feet pointing towards the ceiling. Keeping the same angle at the hips and knees and keeping the back flat to the floor, lower the legs to the side so they touch the floor at 90º to the body. Return to the start position and then lower the legs in the other direction.

Figure 126: Windscreen wipers

Candlesticks

This is an advanced trunk-conditioning exercise that develops eccentric strength in the trunk as well as concentric strength.

• Lie on the floor or a bench with the head, shoulders and upper back flat on the floor, and the trunk flexed so that the pelvis and legs point completely up in the air.

• The hands should be holding something that can act as an anchor point behind the head of the player (see Figure 127).

• From this position, the legs are lowered, slowly and under eccentric control of the trunk musculature, towards the ground. The trunk is not lowered to the ground.

• This lowering continues until the trunk body is in a straight line (see Figure 128).

• From here, the abdominal/trunk muscles contract concentrically and you return to the starting position.

Alternative Candlesticks

This exercise can be further advanced by the addition of a rotational movement in the trunk-lowering phase of the exercise, raising to a parallel position and then rotating to the opposite side on the next repetition.

Figure 127: Candlesticks start position

Figure 128: Candlesticks bottom position

Machines and Free Weights

All of the conditioning lifts recommended in the previous section have been free-weight lifts; these are very important for sports performers. But why shouldn't players begin to develop strength on machines? These machines, after all, have the advantage of allowing the player to be able to train without a spotter in assistance (if a training partner is not available) and they require little technical skill to use. However, the fact that the machine controls the movement of the exercise means that machines eliminate any training of the stabiliser muscles acting around a joint in a lift. They effectively isolate a joint movement in one dimension, whereas the physiological requirements of sport lie with joint stability and strength in three dimensions.

Indeed, joint isolation does not relate well to the concept of specificity, as almost all game skills are multi-joint in nature and strength training needs to promote total body development and inter-muscular coordination of muscles around various joints, in order to reflect the needs of the game. It is for this reason that strength-training sessions should focus on multiple-joint lifts that stress the entire body and that do not focus on individual body parts. Two to three sessions of such workouts per week also allow every body part to receive quality workouts rather than just one. Similarly, machines encourage detraining of the core postural muscles that control pelvic, trunk and shoulder stability, leading to postural instability – a poor base from which to develop limb power and one that could possibly lead to lumbar back pain in many adolescent and adult players. Therefore, the focus of an effective strength-training programme should be based on the use of free weights.

Weight Training and Physical Maturity

One of the most frequently asked questions by coaches and parents revolves around the age at which someone should begin to use weights in their resistance training. Unfortunately, there is no simple answer to this question, for one principal reason: it is accepted that children have individual rates of physical development and many cross-sections of body shape and size can be seen within any one age group. For this reason, chronological age can only be used as a rough guideline for training progression.

It should be remembered that strength is always trainable in a child of any age. In younger children, this can be developed through activities such as Swiss (physio) ball work, body-weight control exercises (such as the traditional press-up, squat thrusts, bench dips and sit-ups) and medicine-ball exercises. There is, however, a recognised appropriate time to begin strength training in both males and females. This key period of development for strength relates to the onset of puberty and can be measured through the period known as *peak height velocity of growth* (PHV), more commonly referred to as the *teenage growth spurt*.

The pre-adolescent years can be characterised by poor coordination, due to the accelerated development of the nervous system during rapid growth stages. However, free-weight techniques are skilled movements that need to be learnt to benefit the dexterity of the young player. In Britain, we have traditionally been held back in our development of young individuals for too long, by having an over-developed sense of caution about the general use of strength training, particularly with weights, which has prevented children undergoing this vital learning stage. When children undergo this training, after having reached the appropriate stage of development to work with resistive masses, they already have a well-developed technique base. For many adult players, the lack of development of a safe and effective technique is the biggest barrier to being able to train with weights effectively.

Prior to PHV, strength gains occur largely as a result of neurological improvements. Strength gains can be aided by the young player learning the techniques and movements of free-weight lifting. This can be achieved by learning and practising the techniques with a broomstick, and need not involve lifting any significant mass. However, as technical competency improves, the resistive mass of the bar can be progressively and gradually increased, so that the athlete is working against progressively increasing loads and developing strength and athletic potential.

It has long been thought by coaches, parents and teachers that young athletes should not lift weight until they have gone through the adolescent growth spurt. Lifting weight prior to this was thought to cause such detrimental effects as stunting children's growth, or damaging the epiphysial plates (growth plates) in the bones through shearing or compressing forces. However, it is clear from researched principles and anecdotal evidence that this simply isn't true, and that improving a young player's potential through weight lifting is a valuable aid to athlete development (Byrd et al., 2004).

Figure 129: Instruction of young judo players by Dr Kyle Pierce of the US Weightlifting Development Centre at a sportscotland workshop

A parent or coach monitoring the height of their child on a regular basis can measure the onset of PHV fairly easily. In females, once PHV has begun, the individual is able to begin to progressively build upon her developed free-weight training technique. She can gradually increase the mass lifted in order to progressively overload her neuromuscular system and maximise strength gains. In males, the time to optimise such training occurs after some 12–16 months after the onset of PHV, at a time when testosterone levels are at their highest.

Age apart, it should be remembered that poorly planned, poorly performed and over-strenuous resistance training is as dangerous for adults as it is for children. Whether working with a child or an adult, it is important to realise that technique needs to be taught and training needs to be supervised by an experienced and knowledgeable coach. The coach should be educated and qualified according to the standards of the UK Strength and Conditioning Association and work in an appropriately managed environment.

How Much to Lift and How Many Times

As identified in Chapter 2, the size-recruitment principle of muscle fibres is important in designing a strength-training programme. To fully develop the Type IIx fibres that are essential for power production, the weight lifted needs to be very heavy or the movement very powerful. This nature of weight is not going to be lifted many times, however. This is where the concept of the repetition maximum (RM) (Fleck and Kraemer, 1997) becomes important, as it relates to the maximum number of repetitions that can be completed with a given load. For example, a 1 RM of 100 kilograms in an identified lift means that a player can lift a maximum (single lift) of 100 kilograms. Similarly, a 3 RM of 70 kilograms means that this weight can be lifted a maximum of three times.

RM 1	3	6	10 12	20	25	35
	Power		Strength	Endurance		→

Figure 130: The theoretical repetition maximum (RM)[24]

This information can be used to shape how the strength-training programme is put together, by manipulating the number of times the weights are lifted (repetitions) and the number of blocks of repetitions that are completed (sets) per exercise.

Table 4: General guidelines for constructing a training session

Objective	Repetitions per Set	Suggested Recovery Time Between Sets
Power	1–3	3–8 mins
Strength	5–8	3–5 mins
Strength and size increase	8–10	2–3 mins
Strength–Endurance (Not a necessary focus for game-based sport-specific training)	15+	0–3 mins

In order to develop power, it is important to train all of the fibre types. However, imagine that you are lifting the heaviest weight that you possibly can (your maximal lift) – will this be a fast or slow movement? The answer must be that, despite using all of the fibre types, the movement will be slow. There is a definite need to combine these maximal lifts with an element of speed. Generally speaking, there should never be any reason to intentionally attempt to lift a weight slowly: players should always be encouraged to lift as rapidly as possible. However, with the lower repetitions, it is not always possible to lift the weight rapidly, no matter how hard a player tries, as has already been identified. So how does this develop power? This is done by manipulation of the weight that the player lifts, to allow explosive speed to develop, which is achieved through training[25] using between 50% of a player's one repetition maximum (1 RM) (eg in a snatch lift), 70% of the 1 RM (eg in a squat clean) and 80% 1 RM (eg in a squat) and lifting this weight explosively. This allows peak power (ie force x velocity) to be generated, as shown in Figure 131.

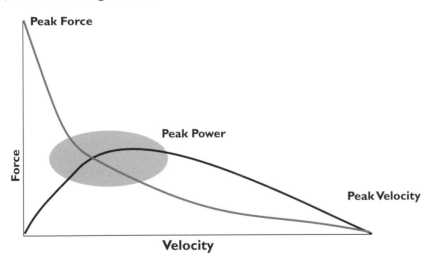

Figure 131: The relationship between peak force, peak velocity and peak power

Testing Strength

As with any aspect of fitness, monitoring and testing the strength/power development of a player is one of the primary functions that a coach can fulfil. These tests provide the coach with a range of information that is essential in programme planning. Firstly, the tests should provide baseline data about how strong the athlete is prior to commencing the programme. This is essential, as a coach needs to be able to determine whether the programmes being implemented are working or not, and how much progress each individual athlete is making. Therefore, tests to assess the current status of an athlete are also needed periodically. The data from these tests not only allows the coach to determine what strengths and weaknesses to work on, but also to set objective goals for the athlete to work towards. Such examinations can be formal – planned months in advance, as part of a long-term programme – or they can be more spontaneous, allowing the coach to test the current situation. Whatever the circumstances, the test should conform to certain rules in order to be effective. These rules are as follows. Tests must:

- replicate the competitive demand of the sport (ie test biomechanically similar movements)

- be simple and repeatable, so that there can be a realistic comparison between test results over time

- be interpretable (ie the coach must understand the implications of the results and rapidly apply them to the developed training programme).

The standard form of testing strength is to record a repetition maximum for a given lift. For example, 5 RM in developing athletes and 1 RM to 3 RM in players who are fully competent technically. The standard lifts used in the majority of game-based sports are one or two lifts from clean, snatch, squat and bench press, as an indicator of upper-body strength. This is because the multiple-joint actions of these lifts are biomechanically similar to many of the actions required within a multitude of sports.

The most common repetition maximum tested in sports is either 3 or 5. This is because very few sports require maximal strength to be tested in a one-off situation. However, to test using more than 5 repetitions means that the explosive power elements important to the sport will not be tested adequately, and it is consequently not a valid test for the sport.

Once the appropriate lift and the required repetition range has been determined, the player should warm up appropriately, and begin by lifting 50% of their required repetition maximum. For example, if someone has a 3 RM squat clean of 80 kilograms, they should begin by lifting 40 kilograms for 3. After a 3–5-minute rest, this should be progressed to 80%, then 90% and then 100%, and so on, until the player cannot complete the required number of repetitions safely (and with sound technique) with the given weight. It is important to allow adequate recovery between attempts and also to not have too many attempts before maximum, in order to avoid unnecessary fatigue. The last weight to be successfully lifted for the given number of repetitions should be recorded.

It is important that coaches using testing of this type are confident in the technique of the player tested. If their technique is at all unstable, testing of this kind should not be used and the simple monitoring of training lifts as technique develops will provide coaches with sufficient data. Similarly, such tests must not be used if a player's training status is not 100% (ie they are nursing an injury or they are fatigued). Some lifts, such as the bench press or the squat, require competent spotters, to provide assistance in returning the bar to the start position should the lifter fall.

Example Training Sessions

Below are some example sessions taken from different sports. It is important to realise that these are presented as ideas for how coaches can use the exercises shown earlier on in this chapter. Actual programming depends upon many factors, such as the level of the performer, individual training needs and the stage of the season.

Example 1: Rugby Forward

Objectives of session: Build size and strength

Stage of season: Off-season

Training age of player*:   2 years

Exercise	Number of Sets	Number of Reps	Weight to Lift (% RM)	Movement	Duration of Rest Between Sets (Mins)
Push press	4	5	100	Explosive	4
Squat	4	8	100	Explosive	5
High pull (snatch grip)	4	8	100	Explosive	5
Bench press	4	8	100	Explosive	3
V-sits	4	10	–	Explosive raise, controlled lowering	3

*how long this person has been lifting weights

Example 2: Soccer

Objectives of session: Develop speed and strength

Stage of season: Late pre-season

Training age of player: 6 years

Exercise	Number of Sets	Number of Reps	Weight to Lift (% RM)	Movement	Duration of Rest Between Sets (Mins)
Overhead squat	4	6	100	Controlled descent, explosive ascent	3–5
Push jerk	4	4	70	Explosive	3–5
Split clean	4	3	70	Explosive	5–8
Stiff-legged deadlift	4	6	100	Controlled descent, explosive return	3
Candlesticks	4	10	–	Explosive raise, controlled lowering	3

Example 3: Tennis

Objectives of session: Develop explosive speed

Stage of season: In competition

Training age of player: 3 years

Exercise	Number of Sets	Number of Reps	Weight to Lift (% RM)	Movement	Duration of Rest Between Sets (Mins)
High pull (clean grip) from high hang	3	4	70	Explosive	5–8
Squat snatch	4	3	30	Explosive	5–8
Split jerk	4	3	50	Explosive	5–8
Single-leg squat (lunge) with multi-directional leg movement	3	6	40	Explosive return to start position	5

Summary

Important points for players:

- Control the weight; do not let it control you. Lower the weight in a controlled fashion, while raising the bar in an explosive, powerful manner.

- Make sure that you are familiar with the correct technique for a lift. Most injuries occur because people lift weights that are too heavy for them and/or they use incorrect technique. Egos in the gym do not improve performance. Therefore, do not attempt to lift weights to impress others – stick to your own limits. Do not follow the MOR-ON school of thought – ie thinking you'll put more weight on the bar, before being technically prepared for the extra kilograms.

- Before you attempt any lift, always check that the equipment you are using is fully functional and not damaged in any way. Always make sure that the plates on a dumb-bell/barbell are secured with a suitable collar if appropriate.

- Intensity is the key to successful training. Maintain 100% intensity and concentration throughout the session.

- Train with a partner for safety and motivational purposes. Spotters can also aid your lifting by helping you to complete repetitions that you find difficult, thus helping you *lift to failure* (ie train maximally).

- Never train in cramped conditions. Ensuring that you have enough space for a safe lift means that you will not endanger yourself or others while training.

- Allow adequate rest (3–8 minutes) between sets of lifts involving major muscle groups. Lifts using smaller muscle groups do not need the same amount of recovery time.

- Do not ignore the conditioning of the abdominals and lumbar back, or the development of the postural muscles that control pelvic and core stability.

- Strength and power are the changeable elements that can greatly influence the success of a sports performer at any level.

References

Brewer, C., Favre, M. and Low, L. (2005) 'Weight lifting for sports specific benefits', http://www.coachesinfo.com/category/strength_and_conditioning/

Fleck, S.J. and Kraemer, W. J. (1997) *Designing Resistance Training Programmes*. Illinois: Human Kinetics. ISBN: 0-873221-13-3.

Stone, M.H. (2000) 'Explosive exercise and training', *National Strength and Conditioning Association Journal*, 15 (3): 7–15.

Stone, M.H. (2002) 'How strong is strong enough?', http://www.coachesinfo.com/article/index.php?id=246&style=printable

Stone, M.H. (2005) 'The use of weightlifting pulling movements in sports', paper presented at The UK Strength and Conditioning Association Conference, Loughborough, May 2005.

Further Information

Brewer, C. and Stone, M.H. (2005) 'Coaching the double knee bend', http://www.coachesinfo.com/category/strength_and_conditioning/

Byrd, R., Baker, C., Pierce, K. and Brady, J. (2004) 'Young weightlifters' performance across time', http://www.coachesinfo.com/category/strength_and_conditioning/245

Stafford, I. (2004) *Coaching for Long-term Athlete Development*. Leeds: Coachwise Business Solutions/The National Coaching Foundation. ISBN: 1-902523-70-9*.

Stone, M.H. (1990) 'Muscle conditioning and muscle injuries', *Medicine & Science in Sport & Exercise*, 22 (4):457–62.

* Available from Coachwise 1st4sport. For a full range of sports education and training equipment, please visit www.1st4sport.com or call 0113-201 5555.

Chapter 5
Plyometric Training

Introduction

Power (mass x acceleration) is a work rate (distance/time). Rate of force development is the ability to produce maximal muscular forces very rapidly, and this is very important in sports that rely on the acceleration component for powerful movements and skills.

Plyometrics are specialist exercises that enable a muscle to reach maximal strength in a short space of time. This works by stimulating the stretch reflex: stretching a muscle and then relying on its elastic properties to produce greater forces than are normally possible in the reflex contraction (as the muscle returns to its resting length). In order to achieve this greater muscular force, the muscle must contract, following lengthening, within the shortest possible time.

Table 5: How does a plyometric work?

	Eccentric Phase	Amortisation Phase	Concentric Phase
Demonstration			
Action involved	The prime mover (agonist muscles) is stretched.	Transition phase between eccentric and concentric phases. This should be as short as possible for the action to be effective.	The muscle fibres in prime movers are shortened.
Results of action	Potential energy is stored in the muscles and connective tissue. Stretch receptors within the muscle are stimulated.	Stretch inhibitors send signal to the central nervous system, and this stimulates concentric contraction of agonist muscles.	Elastic energy is released from muscles and connective tissue. Prime movers are stimulated to forcefully contract concentrically.

The following drills on page 97 use dynamic movements to achieve this stretch-shortening in a muscle, thus causing a faster concentric (reflex) contraction of the muscle. Many people design plyometric routines that have a basis in track and field, such that they are based upon straight-line actions. However, this is not representative of the performance demands of game-based sports. What is more, plyometric drills need to be multi-dimensional in nature (ie incorporate lateral and forward/backward movement).

Coaches need to ensure that their player's body is suitably developed (ie that their muscles have a good strength base) and is well trained before attempting such exercises. For example, the National Strength and Conditioning Association (NSCA) recommends that the individual is able to squat 1.5 times their body weight before undertaking high-intensity plyometric training. Technique is very important. Bad coaching and poorly executed technique lead to injuries.

Coaches should use the following guidelines as an aid to coaching, and not a replacement for strength-training instruction or experiential learning opportunity facilitated by a suitably qualified and experienced individual. Individuals with a history of stress-induced injuries to the feet, ankles, shins, knees, hips or lower back should not perform plyometric activities without consulting a chartered physiotherapist.

Classification of Plyometric Exercises

Jumps

These can be either *in-place jumps* (taking off and landing on the same spot) or *standing jumps* (which emphasise either horizontal or vertical components of movement from a stationary/standing position). Jumps begin and end with one or both feet and are usually performed in sets of 5–8 repetitions. Jumps form the lowest intensity of plyometric exercises and include many basic exercises such as skipping. *Box jumps* increase the intensity of the exercise by giving the player something to jump off, over or on to. The height of the box depends upon the size and strength of the athlete and the goals of the programme.

Hops

Hops begin and end with the player on one or both feet and are associated with a component of maximum horizontal distance. Training volume is usually measured by sets of 5–8 reps or by distance (ie covering 40–60 metres over a series of movements in a set). These are low- to medium-intensity exercises, although intensity can be augmented by increasing the vertical component of the hop (eg hopping over something).

Bounds

Bounds are the alternating movements associated with take-off from one foot and landing with the other, in repetitive sequence, usually with the aim of covering as much distance between each ground contact as possible. These are classified as medium-intensity exercises and are usually undertaken in sets of 5–8 reps, or by covering a distance (eg 60–80 metres).

Shocks

These are very high-intensity plyometrics, which will place significant stress on the neuromuscular system and connective tissues. Shocks usually constitute an element of *depth jumping* (ie jumping down from a raised platform, a 40-centimetre-high box) and will have either a vertical component (ie jumping down and then up) or a horizontal component (ie jumping down and then out). This uses gravity and the athlete's weight to increase exercise intensity. Only an experienced performer who is sufficiently well trained to cope with the high stresses associated with shock training should undertake training of this nature. The platform height will vary according to the age, weight, training status and experience of the performer.

Coaches should not undertake shock plyometrics with players who do not have a well-developed strength base and are not in excellent physical condition prior to commencing the programme. As a general guideline, players over 100 kilograms in weight should not perform depth jumps from heights exceeding 50 centimetres.

Intensity of Plyometric Training

The intensity of a plyometric exercise can be reduced by lowering the centre of mass in a jump (ie starting from a bent-over position). They can be made more intense by decreasing the surface area of body contact (eg landing on one foot rather than two) or increasing either the horizontal or vertical distance jumped (ie additional vertical components place more stress on the performer than increased horizontal ranges of a jump).

All of the horizontal and vertical movements described within this chapter can be made more difficult by performing them with the addition of a bungee cord. This should be tied around the waist and tensioned in the start position. Resistance provided laterally will increase the postural control that the advanced performer will need to demonstrate in executing the movement. Resistance to the direction of movement (ie from behind in a horizontal jump, anchored to the floor in a vertical jump) will increase the amount of force necessary to complete the movement.

Progression

Plyometrics are skill-based, high-speed movements and as such can only be done when the player is in an unfatigued state. This means that plyometrics need to be scheduled towards the start of a training week and at the start of training sessions, when the player is still fresh. Coaches should progress plyometric training from exercises of low intensity through to high intensity, following the principle of progressive overload. This should apply over a number of weeks, but also within individual sessions.

Some low-intensity plyometric exercises (eg single-leg hopping on the spot with the eyes closed) are excellent to incorporate into the warm-up routine, in order to activate the body's internal sensory (proprioceptive) systems and stimulate the muscles around the ankle and foot joints.

Plyometric activities are ideal for off-season training, following the period of strength development. Shock and higher-intensity plyometrics should not be used during periods when the playing or training volume is high, due to the recovery time that the body needs after each session. Low-intensity plyometrics and medicine-ball drills are, however, ideal for such times. Plyometrics take a relatively longer time period to recover from than other training methods. Recommended frequencies therefore range from one session per week (low-intensity work with beginners) to three low-intensity sessions per week in an experienced performer. Very-high-intensity sessions may take up to 10 days to fully recover from.

Training Volume

Plyometric sets should comprise between 3 and 10 reps (the higher the intensity of the exercise, the lower the number of repetitions per set), with complete recovery (3–8 minutes) between sets.

The following guidelines are based upon the principles outlined by the NSCA. Beginners should start off with no more than 70 foot contacts per session, and gradually progress up to 100. Intermediate players (or advanced players with large body masses) should utilise 100–120 foot contacts per session. Advanced players should work between 120–140 foot contacts in one session. Coaches should remember that plyometric work is about quality of performance, and should therefore not exceed these totals, and allow plenty of recovery time in between sets.

Plyometric Technique

In plyometric exercises that involve landing on the feet, the coach needs to pay particular attention to the position of the foot upon landing. It is important that the player does not contact the ground heel-first for two main reasons. Firstly, this increases the impact forces that travel up through the ankle joints into the knees and lower back, and secondly, this is a very slow position from which the player can accelerate into the next position. The best way to do this is to accelerate the body by pushing off from the balls of the foot. However, in plyometrics where there is a high vertical component of downward force in landing, if the player attempts to land on the balls of the feet, the mass of the body (being accelerated into the floor by gravity) will cause the heels to come down into the floor and bring the centre of mass of the player back onto the heels. From this position, little upward and forward acceleration is possible. However, landing in a flat-foot position will not cause the heel to be driven into the floor in the same way, and the centre of mass can remain above the balls of the feet, allowing rapid acceleration in whichever direction is required in the movement. In this type of exercise, athletes should therefore land flat footed. However, if there are reduced vertical components to this force, and/or the player can control landing on the balls of the feet without the heel being lowered onto the floor, then this should be encouraged by the coach.

Plyometric movements should be fluid in nature. When landing/taking off, the player needs to ensure that the hips are over the feet and the chest is over the knees. As with sound weight-lifting technique, the knees need to move along the same line as the toes[26]. If the knees start to collapse inwards upon landing, due to weak muscles or poorly executed technique, it will result in injury.

It should also be remembered that plyometrics are, for the most part, total-body exercises and so jumping and bounding with the legs should be accompanied by upper-body action. Jumps that use arm drive can be 35% higher than jumps that are from the legs only. The aim is for the player to generate as much height and distance as possible and, therefore, unless directed otherwise, the player should utilise every limb to generate power in the exercise.

Medicine-ball Exercises

These exercises may require a significant amount of space to perform. Adequate care should be taken to ensure the safety of the environment and persons around the player when undertaking the throwing of medicine/jelly (weighted rubber) balls. Working with a partner, to allow the ball to be retrieved, may be beneficial in these sessions.

These are low-impact plyometric exercises that can be incorporated easily into many different types of sporting actions and programmes. The basic idea is to generate power from a stretch-reflex movement that will force the ball away from the player in whichever direction is desirable.

Underhand Throw

The player squats down into a squat position, holding a medicine/jelly ball (henceforth *the ball*) with an undergrasp grip between the legs. From here, the player explodes into a vertical jump, throwing the ball as far in the air in front of them as possible. The aim is to achieve maximum height and distance.

Figure 132: The squat position

Figure 133: The vertical jump and throw

Viking Throw

This is similar in nature to the underhand throw, but the direction of the ball release is different. The player squats down, holding the ball with an undergrasp grip between the legs. From this position, the player explodes into a vertical jump, throwing the ball as high in the air behind them as possible.

Figure 134: Viking throw release

Ball Slam

The player stands tall, with knees slightly flexed, holding the ball above the head. Using as much force as possible, the ball is thrown to the floor so that it lands directly in front of the player, who should catch the ball as it rebounds up. Repeat in sequence.

Figure 135: Ball slam start position

Figure 136: Ball slam

Trunk Rotation

The player stands straight, with feet shoulder-width apart and with the ball in two hands, to the right-hand side of the body. Keeping the arms straight, the player twists further to the right, leading with the hips, and then forcefully reverses the twist to the left and releases the ball, with the aim of throwing it as far as possible. This is repeated by twisting to the other side.

Figure 137: Trunk rotation start position

Figure 138: Trunk rotation release position

Chest Pass

The player stands with feet shoulder-width apart and knees slightly bent. The ball is thrown to the player, who catches it and guides it back to the chest with both hands behind the ball. Explode the ball as far forward as possible. Perform 5–8 reps. This can also be adapted to a further partner drill with the ball being forced downwards against the floor as hard as possible, so that it bounces on the floor mid-way between two players. It can also be adapted so that the ball is forced from the chest position as high as possible between two players.

Figure 139: Receive ball **Figure 140: Amortisation phase (transition from catch to forward push)** **Figure 141: Explode forwards**

Seated Chest Pass

This is carried out as above, but from a seated, inclined trunk position. The player sits on the floor, with legs out in front of the body. The trunk is leant backwards, until the angle between the back and the floor is approximately 45°. The player brings the ball to the chest, with both hands behind it, and explodes the ball as far forward as possible.

Chopping Wood

This drill can be done in pairs (with the partners standing approximately 10 metres apart), or as an individual drill. The feet should be shoulder-width apart and the trunk upright. The player holds the ball in both hands and rotates from the hips to bring the ball around to a point above the head (see Figure 143), and then forcefully propels the ball to the floor, either at an angle if throwing to a partner (see Figure 144) or straight into the ground if training as an individual. If training individually, the player catches the rebound and performs the exercise rotating in the other direction.

Figure 142: Start position **Figure 143: Hip twist, bring ball over head** **Figure 144: Forcefully throw ball to floor**

Back Slam

The player starts by standing upright, with the feet shoulder-width apart and the ball held above the head. From here, the player forcibly contracts the hamstring muscles (to cause knee flexion) and at the same time the ball is slammed down to the floor, as hard as possible, behind the back.

Figure 145: Hold ball above head

Figure 146: Slam ball to the ground

Kneeling Serve

The player assumes a single-leg kneeling position (alternating the forward leg) and keeps the trunk upright. The ball starts directly above the head in two hands. Keeping the arms and the trunk straight and the head up, the player extends the shoulder back as far possible and then explodes the ball forwards as far as possible. The kneeling position ensures that this stays as an upper-body exercise.

Figure 147: Single-leg kneeling position

Figure 148: Explode the ball forwards from above the head

This exercise can also be performed as a single arm exercise, with the emphasis on maintaining pelvic neutral position and keeping the hips level throughout the movement.

Figure 149: Single-arm version using opposite forward leg

Figure 150: Using the arm and leg on the same side

Hip Flexor Throw

The player stands with the ball between both legs, clasped by the anklebones. Keeping the pelvis in the neutral position, the hips are explosively flexed and at the highest point the ball is released so that it is thrown forward as hard as possible into the arms of a partner.

Figure 151: Ball clasped between ankles

Figure 152: Extending the hip and the trunk

Figure 153: Ball thrown forwards by flexing hips

Rotation Drive

This is a drill for one, two or three players. The working player starts sitting down, with legs out in front and slightly bent. A server throws the ball from the left or right so that it can be caught in front (Figure 154). Using the momentum of the ball, when caught, rotate away from the server and touch the ball to the floor (Figure 155). From here, forcefully rotate the ball back to the other side of the body and touch the ball down (Figure 156). Immediately, rotate back to the other side and throw the ball as forcefully as possible (Figure 157).

This drill works best when there are two servers (one on either side of the working player) so that the drill progresses continuously. With two players, the server's throw and player's release need to be in the same direction, so that there will be one less rotation movement. One player can perform this drill by throwing the ball against a wall.

Figure 154: Receiving the ball from the left

Figure 155: Twisting to the other side

Figure 156: Forcefully twisting, from the trunk, back again

Figure 157: Twisting back to the right and exploding the ball away

Hamstring Curl

A hamstring curl is another excellent movement to complement heavy-resistance training in a complex drill (eg following a stiff-legged deadlift – see notes on complex training later in this chapter). The working player lies face down on the floor with the knees extended and the feet together. The spotter should stand so that they straddle the player, slightly in front of the player's head and facing the player's feet. The spotter rolls the ball down the middle of the legs with sufficient force that it will stay on course and roll up the calf muscles (Figure 158). As the working player senses the ball reaching the area of the Achilles tendon (base of the calf muscle) the player should rapidly flex the knee joint, thus firing the ball upwards and into the hands of the spotter (Figure 159).

This will also test the player's proprioception and coordination (without which, the firing of the ball will not take place). The spotter should ensure that the fired ball does not fall down onto the player's body or head.

Figure 158: The ball is rolled down the legs

Figure 159: The ball is fired up to the hands of the spotter

Medicine-ball Tennis

This is a game for two to four players that involves the medicine ball being fired across the net (or training area) to score points, in the same way as tennis. The service lines and court markings can be changed to reduce/increase the stress to the player, depending upon the mass of the ball and the power of the players. Each shot should be caught after one bounce, then the player twists with the shot (ie if the ball comes on the backhand side, the player should catch and rotate to the fullest possible range of motion for a backhand shot) and then explodes the ball back over the net. Drills can be set up to achieve the same effect, but they should be kept as *open* as possible, allowing the player to play shots from various foot and body positions.

Figure 160: Medicine-ball tennis

Figure 161: A steel-reinforced wall in the gym at the All-England Lawn Tennis Club allows players to train for explosive power and warm up dynamically during the Wimbledon tennis championships

Plyometric Exercises

It is important that the coach remembers that all of the following exercises are subject to the variations in intensity that have been outlined earlier on in this chapter.

Jumps

Countermovement Jumps

The player squats down into a quarter-squat position and then explodes upwards as high as possible, using the whole body to generate maximum vertical force.

This can be performed as a repetitive action (one jump straight into the next), with a tuck position at the highest point of the jump (ie a *tuck jump*), or with a pike position (ie a *pike jump*) encouraging the player to adapt the movement position. The player can also use this as a test of ability to jump with maximum vertical height (ie a *standing vertical jump*) or maximum horizontal power (ie a *standing long jump*).

Figure 162: From standing into countermovement position

Figure 163: Maximum countermovement jump

Figure 164: Tuck jump top position

Figure 165: Pike jump top position

Standing Box Jump

From the countermovement position (see Figure 162), the player jumps from a position of approximately 60 centimetres away onto a box or over a hurdle. The height of the box/hurdle is determined by the training status of the player (the usual range is 40–70 centimetres high).

Figure 166: Box or hurdle jump

Ball Throw to Box Jump

The player stands approximately 60 centimetres back from a box/bench that is 40–70 centimetres high and wide enough to jump onto. Holding the ball with an undergrasp grip between the legs, the player squats down into a countermovement squat and then explodes into a forward jump onto the box/over the hurdle, throwing the ball in the air as far behind as possible (Figure 169).

Figure 167: Start position

Figure 168: Squatting down for ball throw

Figure 169: Throwing and jumping

Figure 170: Landing on the box

Cycled Split Squat Jump

The player stands in the lunge position (ie with one leg fully extended forward and the other behind the midline of the body) with the trunk upright. The player jumps vertically as high as possible, with little or no arm swing. While in the air, the player quickly switches leg position from front to back landing in the lunge position with the legs reversed. This is then sequenced, so that the landing of one jump becomes the start of the next jump. The front leg should be alternated at the start of each new set.

Figure 171: Cycled split squat position

Figure 172: Cycled split squat mid position

This exercise can also be performed between boxes, with a slight height difference between each box. This is a fairly advanced exercise that allows the player to adapt to chaotic landing positions and limb position differences, as would be necessary in a game. The player should alternate the position of the higher box between front and back.

Figure 173: Cycled split squat on uneven boxes

Resisted Horizontal Jump

This drill utilises bungee cords attached to a belt around the waist to provide resistance to the movement. The player performs a standing long jump, as high as possible, against the resistance of the bungee cords. The addition of a resistance will encourage the activation of more nerves in firing more muscles. The player should perform four reps, then remove the resistance and immediately perform two long jumps, as high and long as possible.

This exercise can be made multi-directional by the player jumping towards differently numbered/coloured cones but keeping the location of the bungee anchor the same. This will mean all jumps will be assisted in one direction, but resisted in another. Players can start off jumping around the cones in number order, but to progress this exercise, the coach can call a cone number or colour. This progression adds a *thought element* to the drill, preventing a player from anticipating the next jump.

Figure 174: Resisted horizontal jumps

Clap Press-up

The player starts off in a press-up position – elbows straight, back flat, legs straight and head up. From here, the elbows are flexed, lowering the trunk to the floor. From the lowest position of the movement, the player explodes upwards so that the hands leave the floor. Clap the hands once and repeat upon landing.

Figure 175: Clap press-up

Hops

Double-leg Speed Hop

The player stands in a half-squat position, with feet together. Keeping the feet together at all times is important; if they come apart, the tendency is to touch the feet down at different times and this should be avoided, as it does not train bi-lateral power. Jump upwards and outwards, aiming for as much height and distance as possible. In flight, use a double-arm forward swinging action, as if reaching for a ball, and straighten the body. Land in the starting position and repeat the movement.

Figure 176: Double-leg speed hop landing

Figure 177: Take off for second jump

This can be progressed to a *single-leg hop* and then on to a directional change. *Multi-directional hops* are carried out in response to either a verbal stimulus or a visual stimulus, for example a ball being dropped.

Multi-directional Jumps

The player starts in the middle of a square of four mini-hurdles, between 40 and 70 centimetres in height. The player uses a two-footed take-off and landing, then jumps forward over the hurdle in front of them, immediately springing back to the start position upon landing. Then the player immediately jumps over hurdle to the left, springing straight back into the middle of the square. Minimising the time in contact with the ground (and still facing forward) the player immediately jumps backwards over the hurdle behind them, back into the middle and then to the right, finishing up in the middle. This equates to one set.

The above exercise can be made more difficult by numbering the hurdles 1, 2, 3 and 4. The coach then calls out the direction of the next jump as the player lands. This means that the player is not able to anticipate the direction of the next jump and manipulate landing accordingly. Advanced progression of this drill is to perform the exercise on one leg, then carry out the next set on the other.

Figure 178: Multi-directional jumps

Stair Hop

Using a two-legged take-off and landing, the player hops up a flight of 4–10 steps of 20–40 centimetres in height. To increase the intensity, the player can progress to a one-legged take-off and landing.

Figure 179: Stair hop

Lateral Hurdle Hop

The player stands on one side of a hurdle or cone 30–40 centimetres in height. Using a two-footed take-off, the player leaps sideways over the cone, with as much height as possible, lands on the balls of both feet and immediately jumps back in the reverse direction. If this is too advanced, a simpler version of this exercise involves the use of a step or exercise box: the player hops laterally onto the box, makes quick contact and hops off. Advanced progression of the lateral hurdle hop is to repeat the exercise but work on one leg.

Figure 180: Lateral hurdle hop

Double-leg Zig-zags

Place 4–10, 30–60-centimetre-high hurdles (or lower if necessary) in a zig-zag pattern, with approximately 45–60 centimetres between each hurdle. Keeping the feet together and arms by their side, with elbows flexed to 90°, players use a double-arm action and a double-foot jump, in a diagonal direction, to clear the first hurdle. The player needs to keep the shoulders pointing forward and concentrate on bringing the knees high. On landing, the player immediately takes off, changing direction, and jumps diagonally over the second hurdle. This diagonal continues all along the chain of hurdles for one set.

Variation can be achieved by altering the angle of the hurdles to each other, the height of the hurdles or by alternating between single- and double-leg jumps. In advanced progressions, players can also face different directions and/or jump forwards/backwards in response to a call from the coach.

Figure 181: Double-leg zig-zags

Bounds

Standing Triple Jump

From a standing position, the player performs a countermovement jump (see page 105), as high and far forward as possible. Landing on one leg (alternate between the left and right), the player immediately takes off (again jumping as high and far forward as possible), landing on the other foot. Again, the player immediately takes off and lands as far in front as possible.

Figure 182: Standing triple jump (start)

Figure 183: Standing triple jump (landing 1)

Figure 184: Standing triple jump (landing 2)

Figure 185: Standing triple jump (landing 3)

Alternate Leg Bound

The alternate leg bound involves moving in an exaggerated running style that is characterised by a strong hip and knee drive to a position in which the thigh is parallel with the ground. This can also be completed with a single-arm action (as in running, with the opposite-arm-to-opposite-leg action) or a double-arm action (with both arms swinging together). The player starts with a rocking step: arms by the side and one foot slightly in front of the other, as if the player was about to take a step. From here, the player jumps forward, with as much distance and height as possible. In flight, the player needs to prepare for, and land on, the opposite leg, and take off immediately upon landing. The front leg should be alternated at the start of each new set (typically, a set equates to one series of 6–10 bounds).

Figure 186: Alternate leg bounds 1   **Figure 187: Alternate leg bounds 2**

Shock

Box Jump to Maximum Long Jump

The player stands about 60 centimetres back from a 40–70-centimetre-high box or bench. From here, the player jumps onto the box in an explosive manner, using a double-leg take-off. The trunk should be kept upright and a double-arm forward-swinging motion should be used. As the player lands, they should explode off the box, getting as much height and distance as possible (the arms become important in this action). As soon as they land, the player immediately jumps as far forward as possible (as in a standing long jump). This can be modified so that the player jumps upwards on landing, thus performing box jumps to maximum vertical jumps.

Figure 188: Take-off from box   **Figure 189: Maximal long jump upon landing**

Depth Jump to Box

Place 4–8, 40–70-centimetre-high wooden boxes 1–2 metres apart (using boxes or benches that are wide enough to jump onto). The player stands about 60 centimetres back from a box/bench. From here, the player jumps onto the box in an explosive manner and uses a double-leg take-off, keeping the trunk upright and using a double-arm forward swinging motion. As soon as the player lands, they should jump off the box. The higher the jump, the more intense the landing impact will be for the player. This will require some experimentation – make sure that, when the boxes are set up, there is adequate room between them to allow the player to jump appropriately. On landing on the ground, the player immediately jumps onto the next box, and this is continued along the line of boxes.

Variation can be achieved by altering the height of the boxes, the distance and angle between boxes, and by alternating between single- and double-leg take-offs.

Figure 190: Depth jumps between multi-height boxes

Depth Jump to Hurdles

Place a hurdle 1–2 metres away from a 40–70-centimetre-high box. The player jumps off the box, keeping the knees very slightly bent in the air. Landing appropriately, with the legs shoulder-width apart and knees flexed upon landing, the player then immediately explodes over the hurdle. The arms should swing as high as possible in a forward direction, and propel the body as high as possible, concentrating on maximal effort.

Variation can be achieved by obtaining two vaulting boxes of similar (and appropriate) height, and placing the second one after the hurdle. After clearing the hurdle, and upon landing, the player then jumps onto the other vaulting box. This may require someone spotting the player as they land on the second box, to ensure that the player doesn't fall off on landing.

Advanced progressions of this drill incorporate directional changes as the player lands. For example, the player clears the hurdle, jumps backwards over it (or another hurdle placed laterally), lands and explodes onto another box.

Figure 191: Depth jump to multi-hurdle jumps

Depth Jump to Power Twist

This drill begins with the player standing on top of a box in front of a series of 4–6 mini hurdles (20–30 centimetres high) in preparation for an in-depth jump to the floor. The player then performs an in-depth jump from the box. On landing, the player immediately jumps up in the air and performs a 90° turn as they clear the first hurdle. On landing, the process is repeated, but the second jump is through 180° as the second hurdle is cleared, and so on through the sequence until all the hurdles have been cleared.

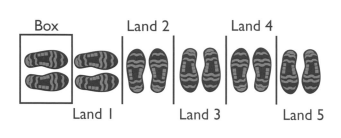

Figure 192: Landing pattern for depth jump to power twists

Figure 193: Power twist shock jumps

Abdominal *Down and Up*

This is a shock plyometric for the abdominal and trunk musculature. The player needs to work with a spotter and lie flat on the floor, with the spotter standing behind the player's shoulders. The player's head should be on the floor, mid-way between the spotter's legs, and holding the spotter's ankles for support. The player bends the legs slightly and then flexes the hip joint until the feet point towards the sky. Maintaining a neutral pelvis and back position, the spotter pushes the player's legs towards the ground in a forceful manner. The player should allow the feet to be accelerated towards the ground, but prevent the feet touching the ground before forcefully returning the legs to the starting position.

This can be advanced by the spotter alternating the angle at which the feet are pushed towards the floor, thus working the trunk musculature through different ranges of motion.

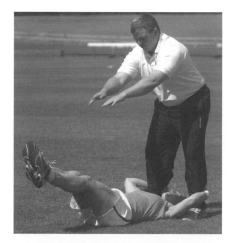

Figure 194: Abdominal *down and ups*

Figure 195: Abdominal *down and ups* with angled pushes

Complex Training

Experienced individuals may wish to combine strength training with plyometric activities. For example, a maximal squat set, followed by a rest of 2–3 minutes, can then be followed by sets of cycled split squat jumps, depth jumps into high jumps, or a bench press followed by a set of explosive chest passes with a medicine ball (after a 2–3-minute recovery period).

This complex training method allows the maximal strength exercises to recruit large numbers of motor units in sports-related movement patterns (refer to Chapter 4) and then the same motor units to be applied to a powerful and explosive movement. Basically, it is a method that tricks the body – the neuro-muscular system is potentiated (activated) by the strength exercises, so that more motor units will be recruited than would be possible voluntarily for the plyometric exercise. This allows the training effect to be maximised.

Summary

Key points to consider when undertaking plyometric training:

• Warm up thoroughly.

• If a player experiences muscular or joint problems, stop immediately.

• Players should wear quality footwear, which provides ankle support and has adequate, but not too much, cushioning in the sole.

• Use a flat landing surface that has good shock-absorbing properties. Surfaces such as sprung-loaded floors are not appropriate - they interfere with the elastic properties of the muscle as it operates in a plyometric exercise. Nor are heavily cushioned surfaces such as a crash mat suitable, as they absorb too much energy and ruin the stretch–shortening mechanism of the exercise. The best surface is a tartan athletics track.

• If boxes or benches are used, make sure they are sturdy and have a non-slip surface.

• Make sure the player has an adequate area for training. Do not put players at risk from obstacles (or others) that may encroach onto their activity.

• The work should be of a high quality. Therefore, ensure that players are adequately rested between sets and do not exceed the recommended volume guidelines.

• Technique is very important – if in doubt, seek appropriate expertise. As with sprinting, you should use the ball of the foot to apply force to the floor, in order to accelerate the body off the ground. Care should be taken to ensure a stable landing on a flat-foot position.

Further Reading

Chu, D.A. (1996) *Explosive Power and Strength: Complex Training for Maximal Results.* Illinois: Human Kinetics. ISBN: 0-873226-43-7.

Chapter 6
Developing Speed and Agility

Introduction

In terms of court/pitch coverage, speed relates to traversing the distance between two points in the shortest possible time. Speed development is therefore sport specific; while running speeds may enable a player to intercept a ball (or beat an opponent rapidly), fast limb speed is essential to numerous activities, including striking, kicking and throwing. Speed is the product of reaction time (the time taken to detect and respond to a stimulus) and movement time (the time from the beginning of a movement to its completion). Movement time can be seen as the product of acceleration (the time between the starting movement and reaching top speed) and achieving top speed (the maximum possible amount of metres per second that a player can move).

When undertaking training to improve the speed of players, the coach should consider designing training to improve the elements of reaction time, acceleration, agility and movement technique, all of which should be incorporated into the training programme.

Top speed, which is comprised of stride length and stride frequency, and reached after about 25 metres of movement, is largely unimportant for the some games players. For example, in tennis, players are never required to sprint more than 15 metres at the maximum. Speed work is typically seen as necessary with an element of directional change. The fast bowler in cricket does not necessarily need to have exceptional running speed, since the final approach is rarely undertaken at maximum pace. Nevertheless, the player must be capable of achieving a final, effective bowling action as a consequence of fast, coordinated limb movement. Similarly, goalkeepers in hockey and soccer rarely have to develop good running speed, as they rarely have to cover large distances at maximal speed. They do, however, need rapid limb and total-body speed, so that quick reaction speeds can be achieved whenever the goalmouth is threatened.

There is limited value, therefore, in a coach spending large volumes of time working on developing the correct sprinting technique[27] in performers. However, form running drills that are designed to establish efficient and error-free movement, by emphasising certain components relating to rapid movement (factors which will be outlined in detail later in this chapter), should be incorporated into the training sessions. The most efficient way to do this is to put these into the session warm-ups, as designed by the coach, and these can easily be incorporated into dynamic flexibility routines (see Chapter 7).

Multiple-sprint sports place acute demands on the ability of a player to react and move quickly in all directions, often with an associated change in direction, while maintaining postural control and the ability to strike a ball or opponent effectively. The components of speed that are vital to a sports player are, therefore, acceleration (a component of power) and agility. Speed and acceleration may be the most vital physical abilities (besides sport-specific technique) that influence a player's competitive level.

Training to develop a player's running speed should be aimed at achieving:

- strength and power (through the training methods identified in Chapters 4 and 5)

- efficient movement technique (the body parts must work together in an effective and synchronised manner)

- the efficiency of the anaerobic energy-delivery systems.

The Key Principles

Speed can only be developed by running maximally. Sub-maximal running will not allow the neuromuscular system to adapt to speed training. If the player is not able to run with 100% effort, their speed will not improve.

Maximum speed development should be treated as a skill and should therefore not be developed when fatigued (unlike speed endurance). Therefore, it is essential that sufficient recovery time (eg 2–5 minutes) be allowed between sprint repetitions.

Remember also that speed should be developed sport specifically. Therefore, distances, angles of running and sport-specific equipment (pads, racket, ball) should be incorporated into 25–50% of the sprints (depending upon the number of times the player will be running with/without the equipment during a game), to enable effective transfer to the player's activity in a game.

Sprinting Technique

There are a number of mechanical principles that a sprint coach would seek to coach a sprinter when developing track technique. All of these principles are outlined below and illustrated in the pictures shown in Figure 196, page 120. This demonstrates that there are a lot of similarities between track sprinters, people running with a ball at their feet and people running in a game.

Body Position

Players should have a slight forward lean (10–15 centimetres) after the start. The back should be flat, with the hips tilted forward, and the *Abdominals* should be tight.

Heel Recovery (Rear Heel Kick Action)

Heel recovery is the product of pushing off the ground. Therefore, the greater the running speed, the higher the heel should kick up as the leg moves through the air. The heel should be tight to the butt at the top of the action, with the thigh above the horizontal position. The heel of the recovery leg should travel above the opposite knee, with the toe pulled to the shin (ankle dorsiflexed). Improper height of this action will hinder the speed of the leg turnover.

Preparation for Ground Contact

The toe should be pulled toward the shin (ankle dorsiflexed) in preparation for ground contact. The player should maintain the forward body lean (by not standing up or leaning back) and the top of the thigh should be above horizontal. The player's foot should contact under, or just behind, the body's centre of mass (which will be a point on the ground under the middle of the stomach). Contact between the ball of the foot and the floor should be a pushing motion, as it is this (rather than a pull) that generates the forces for forward momentum.

Ground Contact Phase

The player should force the thigh towards the ground. The foot should be pointed straight ahead and should not pronate (ie inwardly rotate) excessively. The player's foot should contact the ground with the ball of the foot and a flat-footed landing should be used for a sharp change of direction. The body should drive in a straight line, through the action of ankle, knee, hip, shoulder and head. After the player pushes off, the foot motion is one of lift, reach and pull through (as if to reach and then pull back, in a manner that would allow the player to *grab grass* with the ball of the foot).

Arm Action

The player's arms should be flexed to 90–100°, with no elbow flexion or extension in the movement, and should drive in a forward–backward motion about the shoulder joint. There should be minimal lateral movement, which reduces speed by causing shoulder rotation. When driving forwards, the player's hands should not cross the mid-line of the body but should rise to the level of the chin and backwards beyond the hips (the *hips to lips* movement). The elbow drive backward will speed up the leg action, therefore the faster the player moves the elbows, the quicker the player's feet will move.

Coaches can demonstrate this by asking players to keep their hands by their side and jog on the spot. Then, keeping their arms still, get the player's to move their feet as fast as they can. Then, without stopping, ask them to move their arms and feet as fast as they can and note what happens to their leg speed (it will increase!).

Hand Action

The player's hands should be relaxed. While it does not matter, in terms of speed, whether the hands are open or closed, it is hard to imagine anyone being ready to catch a ball (important in many sports) with the hands clenched into a closed fist! Hands that are clenched tightly create tension in the shoulders, which restricts shoulder movement.

Head

The player's head should stay facing forward in a relaxed upright position, to allow the player to monitor what is going on around them, and should not sway in any direction. A stable head position allows the eyes to scan around and make decisions about what is going on in the game in front of them. A swinging head means that this important action is not possible. The player's jaw should be loose and relaxed at all times (hence the term *jelly jaw* associated with sprinting).

Head up: Maintain erect posture and line of sight.

Arm drive from the shoulder, elbows stay bent at 90º, allowing large *Deltoid* muscles to drive the arm action.

High-knee drive into stride allows ankle of recovery (in-flight) leg to clear (travel above) the knee height of the driving leg.

Straight-line body position between head, shoulder, hip, knee and ankle of driving leg.

Minimal distance between recovery leg, ankle and thigh allows faster/more efficient travel of recovery-leg cycle.

Ankle fully extends at the end of the leg drive.

Ankle joint dorsiflexed* in preperation for landing on the ball of the foot

*Toe pulled towards knee

Forward trunk lean during initial phases of acceleration.

Shoulders are relaxed.

Arm action: opposite arm and leg forward/back. Hand of driving arm comes up level with the chin.

Hips are high enough off ground to allow driving leg to extend fully on the ground.

Player pushes off from ball of foot (large surface area) and minimal heel contact with ground

actionplus

Figure 196: The basic components of an efficient sprinting technique

Sound sprinting technique is reliant on the development of the technical consistencies outlined above and in Figure 197. However, not all of these technique points need to be developed in performers from all sports. In short, not every sport requires a sprint performance in order to be successful. For example, a tennis or squash player must run with a racket in hand at all times during the game and, in moving between court positions following shots, the players very often do not reach an upright position. However, key principles relating to moving on the balls of the foot, having the shoulders relaxed and keeping the head up should all be worked on in accordance with the principles of speed development.

Coaches should avoid the phrase 'on your toes' as the toes have a small surface area and do not provide a stable platform from which to exert a force.

The following drills are typically used to develop sprint technique. They can also be incorporated into a warm-up, as part of a dynamic flexibility routine.

(a) Seated Arm Action

Sit with the legs straight and drive the arms in a sprinting motion (as described above) as fast as possible. The faster the arm movement generated, the faster the sprinting leg action will be. Try to lift your butt off the floor using the arm action only.

(b) Down and Off

Stay relaxed (the key to good sprinting) and bring your knees up higher than parallel to the ground, picking up the speed of movement while maintaining a high-knee lift. You should then concentrate on decreasing the amount of contact between the ground and the foot. Hit the ground with the ball of the foot and get off as soon as possible. In turn, the effort on the ground should bounce your leg up into the high-knee position.

(c) Align the Heels

Move in a walking motion, bringing the lead leg through with the ankle in a dorsiflexed (toes to knees) position, with the heels moving as close to the butt as possible. Extend the leg from here in a normal motion. The coach should place emphasis on allowing (but not forcing) the heel to come up to the buttock.

(d) Skips for Height and Distance

Move with an easy, rhythmical, skipping action, working the arms and aiming for long, high skips. The arm swing should be a loose, swinging movement, controlled from the shoulder. Everything should work in a straight line as you move.

(e,f,g) Pull-through

Extend the leg in front of the body (like a hurdler), with the knee raised as high as possible (e). Extend the knee so the leg is straight (f) and then bring the leg down and contact the ground with the ball of the foot slightly behind the trunk, in a powerful motion (g).

(h) Strider Sticks

Place sticks on a grassy surface, starting them 45 centimetres apart and progressively increase this to 2 metres. Use approximately 20 sticks. Sprint through the sticks as fast as possible, touching one foot down between each stick. The foot–ground contact should be as quick as possible and your knee lift should be high. If possible, the coach should record the time between the first and second foot contacts, and the time it takes you to complete the course.

(i) Fast Feet

From a standing start, take as many small steps as possible over a 10-m distance. Then jog for 10 m and repeat. The aim is to get the body used to moving as quickly as possible. The coach should emphasise quick turnover, with the legs moving in front of, not behind or under, the body.

(j) High Knees

In a walking (and later skipping) motion, concentrate on bringing the heel over the knee of the supporting leg, with the ankle in a dorsiflexed position. The coach should ensure that the player walks on the balls of the feet.

(k) Side Drives

Sprint forward, with a lateral movement every three steps. The coach should place emphasis on shifting the body weight onto the driving leg at the point of direction change while maintaining forward motion and speed.

Figure 197: Drills to develop sprint technique

Starting Drills

In game-based sports, players need to be able to quickly react to the opponent's play from a number of different body positions. Common positions include from the floor (after a tackle), going through a transition from walking or jogging, landing on one or two feet (after making a smash or performing a blocking move) or from an extended lunge position (eg after reaching for a drop shot in squash).

The coach needs to recognise the variety of starting positions that are common within the sport that he/she coaches and then incorporate combinations of all of these positions into speed and agility practices in order to ensure that the player is able to maximise their potential explosive development. As with many coaching drills, the only limitation on the variety of these starting positions is the coach's imagination.

Up Tall and Fall

Stand with the feet together and lean forward into a partner (if available), who should take the weight of your body as you lean forward. It is important that a straight line is maintained between the head (which should face forwards), shoulders, hips, knees and ankles as the player leans. This straight-line position, on the balls of the feet, is referred to as the *drive position*. Once the partner has your full body weight, they should step to one side, causing you to fall forward. (If no partner is available, maintain the correct body position and fall forward until the point where you over-balance.) As soon as the support is removed and you fall forward, you should immediately accelerate away. If body position is lost (check that your head is looking forward and that the straight-line body position is maintained) gravity will cause you to fall over!

Figure 198: Up tall and fall

Flying Start

Accelerate into a sprint from a 5-metre jog.

Figure 199: Acceleration from a flying start

Off the Floor

Lie on the floor, facing the direction of play (ie the direction of the sprint) or away from the direction of movement (depending on which is more appropriate for the sport). In one movement, get off the floor, turn and sprint in the required direction.

Figure 200: Getting off the floor

Side Shuffle

Side step left and right between two cones placed 2–5 metres apart, concentrating on moving on the balls of your feet. On an appropriate signal (eg 'Go'), accelerate forwards.

Figure 201: Side shuffle

Figure 202: Acceleration on cue

Partner Jumps

Jump continuously on the spot in varied patterns (eg land feet together, feet apart, feet crossing over) as directed by a partner/the coach. On the command 'Go', or another stimulus, such as a ball drop, break into a sprint. This will enable you to practise moving off any foot.

Figure 203: Partner jumps

Reaction Drills

Speed is the product of reaction time (the time taken to detect and respond to a stimulus) and movement time (the time from the beginning of a movement to its completion). Training a player's reactions is therefore a very important part of training. In a game, players need to react to the visual stimulus, for example, the movement of a ball or another player, as well as possible verbal stimuli, such as 'man-on', or a pre-set call to initiate a move. Therefore, in training, players should practise reacting to this type of stimulus. Reaction drills always need to be done in pairs or larger groups (three or more players) in order to be effective. As with many of the drills outlined in this chapter, these drills lend themselves very well to warm-up sessions for all tennis activities.

Crazy-ball Drills

Take a crazy (reaction) ball[28] and bounce it to a partner, making them move to the direction of the bounce to catch the ball.

Figure 204: Crazy-ball drills

Other games can be invented for the crazy ball, as well as the partner throws outlined above.

Catch Me if You Can **Drill**

Two players face each other, 5 metres apart. Player 1 jogs backwards, Player 2 follows, keeping 5 metres apart. Player 1, when ready, shouts 'Go' and turns and sprints. Player 2 has to catch Player 1 before they run 15 metres. This drill can be varied by Player 2 calling and Player 1 reacting or by a third person calling and both players having to react.

Figure 205: Catch me if you can

Cut-offs

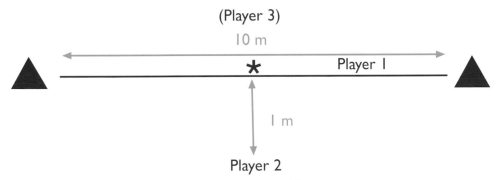

(Player 3)

10 m

*   Player 1

1 m

Player 2

Figure 206: Cut-off set-up

Player 1 starts at the point marked by a * and sprints to one of the markers. Player 2 reacts and tries to cut them off before they reach the marker. Variety can be introduced by having a third person call out 'left' or 'right', thus both players have to react to a verbal stimulus. Similarly, a third person can indicate, using hand signals, the direction of sprint to Player 2. Player 1 then has to react to the movement of Player 2 (see Figure 206). This version can be progressed by having Player 2 side-step left or right within a defined area, in response to hand signals from Player 3. This might involve the following variations: left hand up, side step left; right hand up, side step right; left arm pointing vertically and right arm horizontal, sprint to right cone; left arm horizontal and right arm vertical, sprint to left cone. Player 1 should react to the movements of Player 2 and mirror them appropriately.

Ball-drops

Players can also train reaction times and decision-making in response to visual stimuli, by using ball-drop drills. Two players stand 5 metres apart, facing each other (Figure 207). When Player 1 drops a ball from an outstretched hand, Player 2 accelerates towards the ball and attempts to catch it before the second bounce (Figure 208).

Figure 207: Ball-drops start position

Figure 208: React and catch the ball after one bounce

To develop decision-making skills, use two balls, as follows: Player 1 has a ball in each outstretched hand and drops one of them for Player 2 to react to accordingly. Notice how this necessitates the player changing body position away from the split-step start to a more neutral, two-footed stance, to allow acceleration in either direction in response to the ball-drop.

Figure 209: Decision-making and ball-drops

By introducing more players, a sequence of such decisions-making/reaction-developing opportunities can be practised. Each player should stand 5 metres back from the person in front, and drop their ball as soon as the working player has caught the ball in front. The emphasis is on making the player work to react to the ball-drop: they should not therefore have to wait for the person in front to drop the ball. This will also mean that another player has to be available to catch balls that are caught and passed by the working player. By altering the angle at which the players are placed, these drills can also be used to practise directional change (in accordance with agility practices outlined herein).

Acceleration

Acceleration can be viewed as the ability to rapidly propel a stationary body, or to rapidly increase pace. Acceleration improvement can make a significant difference to the effectiveness of any sports performer. Acceleration is determined by the length of time that it takes a player to reach top speed, and is directly proportional to the application of force to the ground; the greater the force applied, the greater the acceleration. Correct technique is important in developing maximal accelerations, as the body's ability to exert a force will depend upon it being in the correct position. Therefore, it is important that the appropriate drills outlined herein are undertaken in conjunction with the appropriate (multi-joint) resistance-training exercises and plyometric activities.

Below are detailed examples of drills designed to improve a player's acceleration. Coaches should remember that, as well as changing the starting stimulus and position, the angle of sprints should also be adapted (ie design the 5-metre sprints to run diagonally to the left and right, as well as straight on) in order to vary the patterns and make them more representative of the specific game requirements.

Acceleration Sprints

• 10 x 5-metre sprints (100% speed) with active recovery between reps.

• Easy jogging 3 mins.

• 7 x 10-metre sprints (100% speed) with active recovery between reps.

• Easy jogging 3 mins.

• 5 x 15-metre sprints (100% speed) with active recovery between reps.

Hollow Sprints

• Mark a 100-metre course into 20-metre intervals.

• Jog 20 m, sprint 20 m (50% speed), *cruise* 20 m, sprint 20 m, jog 20 m. (Concentrate on changing pace into the sprints.)

- Active recovery.

- Repeat 2 sets of 4–8 reps.

Gear-change Sprints

- Mark out 100 m in 20-metre segments.

- Run between these segments, increasing the pace every 20 m (jog, stride, 75% speed, 90% speed, 100% speed).

- Active recovery.

- Repeat 2 sets of 4–8 reps.

Flying 10s

- Mark out a 30-metre course into a 20-metre section and a 10-metre section.

- Start running at 50% speed and increase the pace with each stride, until you are at full pace by the end of the 20 m. Maintain maximal speed for a final 10 m.

- Active recovery.

- Repeat 2 sets of 6–8 reps.

This can be changed into 40 metres (20-metre acceleration, 20-metre sprint) or other distances, as is relevant for the sport.

Resisted Drills

Some of the drills outlined in this section can be performed with a bungee cord, attached by a harness or belt and with a resistance, either from a person holding a bungee, or a weighted sled (this should not be so heavy that it interferes with technique development). Wearing a weighted vest will also achieve the same effect. If such equipment is not available, a manual resistance (ie a partner hanging on to your hips as you run) can be just as effective, as long as they do not interfere with your movement.

The purpose of such resistance work is to increase the resistance to the sprint. In basic terms, this will require more nerves to fire, thus making more motor units active in the movement. This is not something that can be achieved voluntarily; it will only occur in response to an increased resistance.

However, it is desirable that movement technique does not suffer as a result of this resistance. It is important, therefore, that the resistive load does not add more that 5–10% of body mass to the individual.

It is recommended that you run several successive drills with the resistance added and then, immediately after, run the same pattern without the resistance. This is known as *contrast training*: the neuromuscular system will continue to operate as though the resistance were present, thus training the muscles to operate in that manner all the time. This works in a similar way to the principles of complex training (adding plyometric work to resistance-training sets) and will make the player faster over time.

Agility Drills

Agility can be considered as the ability to precisely and quickly change direction or body position. In most games, all players will be required to undertake directional change quickly and precisely, after many varied distances, with rapid movements (usually between 2 metres and 20 metres). Acceleration is therefore an important part of all agility drills. As well as enhancing a player's performance, good agility training will also aid injury prevention, as the player will be used to rapid and reactive changes of direction.

The following drills form ideal components of warm-ups for all sessions, allowing a player to practise the movements and attain exceptional technique without the need for additional sessions. The drills are also non-fatiguing and so also form ideal rehabilitation /active-recovery sessions.

These drills lend themselves to resisted efforts through the use of bungee cords and harnesses, to facilitate neural recruitment of the optimal number of fast-twitch (explosive) muscle fibres. To achieve maximal training effect using such equipment, unresisted efforts should immediately follow resisted efforts.

All of the following drills should be undertaken with a focus on maintaining good technique: focus on ball-of-the-foot contact, elbows should be angled at 90° and arm drive from the shoulder, ankles are dorsiflexed and the trunk stable.

Rope-ladder Drills

Rope-ladder drills encourage correct foot contact and proprioception, as well as agility. Rope-ladders (with foot holes approximately 30 centimetres square) are excellent tools for this drill but for complete drill adaptability, the coach can chalk or tape the structure on a suitable surface.Rope-ladder drills provide coaches with the opportunity to bring much variety to training

 It should be noted that in all of the following example drills, as the player exits the rope ladder, they should immediately accelerate at 100% pace for 5–10 metres, to allow a contrast effect to occur.

Figure 210: Player using rope ladder

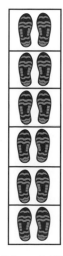

Quick step:

Run through the ladder, putting both feet in every hole along the ladder

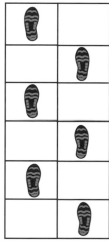

Miss a hole:

Two ladders are placed side by side. Run through, missing out every other hole on the respective left/right side

Figure 211: Rope-ladder drills – quick step

Figure 212: Rope-ladder drills – miss a hole

Side step:

Run sideways along the length of the ladder, putting both feet in every hole.

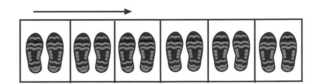

Figure 213: Rope-ladder drills – side step

Lateral push:

Working sideways along the length of the ladder, begin at position a, step forward into the first square of the ladder with the right foot, then follow this with the left foot (position b). Now push off diagonally and backwards with the right foot in a position in front of the next square and follow this with the left foot (position c). Repeat this sequence along the length of the rope ladder. This should be reversed in the next repetition.

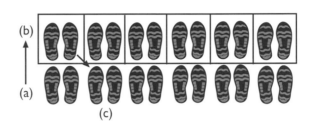

Figure 214: Rope-ladder drills – lateral push

Bunny hops:

Stand with feet together. Bounce through alternate holes, keeping feet together. Spend a minimum amount of time in contact with the ground.

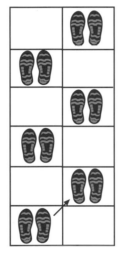

Figure 215: Rope-ladder drills – bunny hops

Cross-steps:

Forward running movement, putting the right foot in every other left hole, and left foot in alternate right holes.

Figure 216: Rope-ladder drills – cross steps

Single-leg hops:

Use two ladders, with a 30-cm space between them. On left foot, hop two spaces forward (a). As soon as possible upon landing, hop one space back (b). Hop diagonally across to other ladder, and land on the right foot (c). Jump two spaces forward (d), back one (e), and across diagonally, to land on left foot (f). Repeat up the ladder.

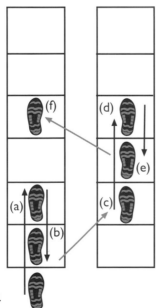

Figure 217: Rope-ladder drills – single-leg hops

Icky shuffle:

From start, put left foot then right foot into hole (a), then left foot out and forward (pushing of with the right foot), followed by right foot (b). Then right foot into hole (c) followed by left. Right foot out and forward (push off with the left), followed by right (d), etc.

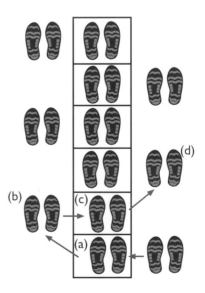

Figure 218: Rope-ladder drills – icky shuffle

Double jumps:

Feet together, jump two holes forward, then one hole back. Repeat pattern up the ladder. Spend as little time in contact with the ground as possible.

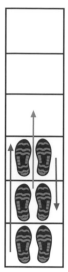

Figure 219: Rope-ladder drills – double jumps

Ladders can be used in many drills as well as in isolation. An example from tennis is shown in Figure 221, which combines an advanced ladder drill (ie directional change in response to a partner's movement, requiring the player's attention to be away from the foot position) with a reaction component and a plyometric drill.

Baseline drives:

Coach (holding medicine ball) moves left or right. Player mirrors directional change in ladder. After 2–8 direction changes, coach throws medicine ball to either their left or right in front of the ladder so that it is 1–2 steps away from the player. This should not be accompanied by any verbal warning, ie this is a visual stimulus. Player explodes out of ladder, picks up ball and throws it explosively (either forehand or backhand) over the net.

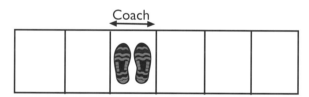

Figure 220: Rope-ladder drills – baseline drives

Progression in all of these drills can be achieved by not looking at your feet, or by having to catch, pass or hit a ball that is being fed to you. When practising these drills on court, you should rapidly accelerate into a 5-metre sprint at the end of every agility drill.

Sport-specific Agility Drills

One of the best things about speed and agility training is that most aspects of this type of training can, and indeed should, be very easily accommodated into the warm-up and technical session drills. Again, the only limitation to the scope and range of reaction, explosion, agility and acceleration practices that can be incorporated into drills is the coach's imagination. The example drills illustrated in the following pages have been modified to allow for the role demands of the individual sports to be trained. The stimulus initiating the player's acceleration also needs to be varied, to allow for the process to be as sport specific as possible.

Some examples follow of agility drills that have been devised for, and used with, players at the highest level in the relevant sports. They are based on the dimensions and markings of the playing area and are designed to replicate various movements that the player may experience during a specific activity. Once again, the basic idea is for the coach to adopt the principles upon which these drills are based and utilise their imagination and knowledge of the game, to devise specific drills to suit particular session or player needs. All of these drills are suitable for inclusion in warm-ups as well as forming the focus of a session. They can also all be adapted for enhanced neuromuscular activation with the use of bungee resistance. Combinations with ladders, or inclusion of other factors such as reaction drills (ie ball-drops), also serve to make these drills progressive, reflective of the actual game and, also, a lot of fun for the players.

Example 1: Tennis

- Player (wearing bungee resistance) starts at X.

- Coach calls out a cone number. Player sprints to the respective cone, (touches cone/plays a shot/throws ball) and returns to X.

- Repeat x 5, with 2 reps unresisted.

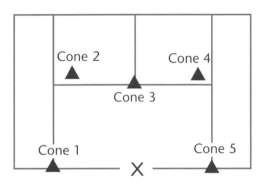

Figure 221: Up and drive

Example 2: Soccer

This drill can be performed by sprinting forward, running backwards or side-stepping. From start, sprint around outside of the circle in an anti-clockwise direction. At cone 1 (or in response to a shouted command), cut in and sidestep straight across circle. When you reach other side, sprint in a clock-wise direction, until 2 (or verbal command), and cut inside again. Vary length of sprints around perimeter.

Alternatives:
- Running forwards, cutting in and out of each cone (emphasise pushing of each foot).

- Running backwards.

- Keeping back squared to inside of the circle, turning and sprinting across circle.

- Keeping front squared to inside of the circle, turn and sprint.

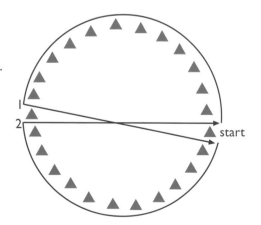

Figure 222: Circle cuts

Example 3: Rugby League

- Start in the ready position.

- Sprint the pattern shown, touching the outside of each line with your foot.

- Sprint to cones 1–5 depending on cue from coach.

- Run the drill in the opposite direction.

- Run the drill laterally (rather than sprinting forward)

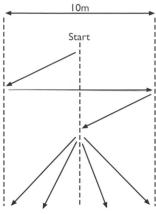

Figure 223: Lateral run

Example 4: Squash

This drill ideally needs two belts and four bungee chords (fixed to the belts on the front, back, left and right sides of the player), which are either held by four people or doubled up and looped around poles/fixed objects to anchor the resistance.
However, this drill can be performed in the same manner without resistance if this is not available. The order of the cones can be randomised in order to progress the complexity of the drill.

- Begin at X
- Sprint forward around A
- Run backwards to B
- Sprint forwards to X
- Sidestep right around C
- Sidestep left across to D
- Sidestep right back to X

Angle of cones can be altered to allow diagonal movements

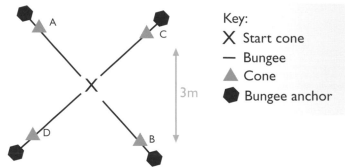

Figure 224: The 4s drill

Coaches should take every opportunity to make training as efficient as possible by integrating agility drills with technical practices. It is essential that the players perform such drills under pressure, in response to match-specific movement patterns and also with sport-specific equipment. Such drills also help to accustom the young performer to the spatial orientation of the playing area. This is important, as spatial awareness is often a deficient quality in pre-adolescents.

Developing Top Speed

This is the maximum speed that players are able to reach. This occurs after the acceleration phase (usually the first 20 metres). Therefore it is best improved by sprinting over longer distances, although again consideration needs to be given to the game/positional role in this. Players should not just run in straight lines during these training sessions, and should incorporate angular and directional changes into such athletic drills as appropriate, to make them more game specific.

Medium-distance Sprints

- 5 x 30-metre sprints   (1 min recovery between each repetition).

- Easy jogging   (3 mins).

- 4 x 35-metre sprints   (1 min recovery between each repetition).

- Easy jogging   (3 mins).

- 6 x 25-metre sprints   (1 min recovery between each repetition).

Pyramid Sprints

The pyramid sprints work primarily on building and maintaining speed.

- 4 x 15-metre then active recovery.

- 3 x 20-metre then active recovery.

- 2 x 35-metre then active recovery.

- 1 x 60-metre then active recovery.

Ensure that each set and rep is followed by active recovery. Reps per distance can be increased by two over a period of weeks.

20-40-60s

- 5 x 20-metre maximal sprints (100% effort) with active recovery between reps.

- Easy jogging 2–5 mins.

- 5 x (2 x 20-metre) maximal sprints with 180° turn (100% effort) with active recovery between reps.

- Easy jogging 2–5 mins.

- 4 x 60-metre maximal sprints (100% effort) with active recovery between reps.

Summary

When designing acceleration and agility practices, there are a number of factors that the coach needs to consider:

- What is the purpose of the drill? This is the fundamental question that will influence all other factors. Once this has been decided, it is important to attend to specific factors such as:

    - In a game, from which starting positions do players have to react quickly?

    - With which stimulus will I start the drills?

- What is the nature of movement required?

    - **Acceleration** (0–20 metres): What angles will the players need to run at/from?

    - **Agility** (direction changes): What is the angle of turns that should be considered; what type of movements; how many direction changes form a typical movement sequence?

    - **Top speed** (20–100 metres): How far will players be required to run in an average sprint in performance (this should comprise the majority of distances in practices) and a maximum distance sprint. To calculate the furthest range for training sessions, add 10 metres to the aforementioned distances.

Coaches should build the carrying of sports equipment (rackets, balls, sticks) into a percentage of the drills undertaken, in order to improve the efficiency of the performer during the game.

Further Reading

Brown, L., Ferrigno, V. and Santana, J.C. (2000) *Training for Speed, Agility and Quickness.* Illinois: Human Kinetics. ISBN: 0-736002-39-1.*

Coachwise 1st4sport (2001) 'Speed Training Drills' video. Leeds: Coachwise 1st4sport.*

Pearson, A. and Hawkins, D. (2005) *SAQ Youth.* A & C Black. ISBN: 0-713670-42-8.*

* Available from Coachwise 1st4sport. For a full range of sports education and training equipment, please visit www.1st4sport.com or call 0113-201 5555.

Chapter 7
Developing Flexibility

Introduction

Flexibility refers to the range of movement (ROM) that is possible around a joint, or a series of joints, in the body. It is important in a games player, as optimum ranges of movement in the musculo–skeletal system can improve a player's performance by increasing the range of a joint movement. The greater the ROM, the more situations the player will be able to perform a skill in and the more skills they will be able to perform. There is also a possibility (less well proved than is commonly thought) that this may also reduce the chances of the player getting injured; this is probably because there is less chance of a player over-extending a joint or muscle during a movement. ROM is limited by a number of things, some of which cannot be directly altered through training, as outlined below:

- **Joint Structure** – Different joints in the body have greater ranges of motion than others, as a joint's structure determines its function and range of movement. Ball-and-socket joints, such as the hip and shoulder, move in all directions, whereas a hinge joint, such as the knee, will only bend and straighten in one direction.

Table 6: The relationship between joint structure and range of movement

Type of Joint	Structure	Example	Normal Movements
Ball and socket	Ball-like head of one bone into the depression of another bone.	• Hip. • *Gleno-humeral* joint in the shoulder.	Three-dimensional: flexion and extension, abduction and adduction, rotation.
Ellipsoidal	Oval-shaped *Condyle* fits into the elliptical cavity of another bone.	• Joints between *Radius*, *Saphoid* and *Lunate* bones in the wrist.	Movement in two planes: flexion and extension, abduction and adduction.
Gliding	Flat surfaces rest against each other.	• The *Carpal* bones in the hand. • Joint between the *Navicular* and *Tarsus* bones in the foot.	Movement in two planes: flexion and extension, abduction and adduction.
Hinge	Concave and convex bone surfaces that fit together.	• Elbow (*Humeral-ulna*). • Knee (*Tibia-femur*). • Ankle (*Tibia-talar*).	Flexion and extension in one plane of motion.

Table 6: The relationship between joint structure and range of movement cont

Type of Joint	Structure	Example	Normal Movements
Pivot	Rounded or pointed surface articulates with a ring structure formed by a bone or bone and ligament (ie a peg through a hole).	• *Atlas* and *Axis* vertebrae in the cervical spine. • Proximal (nearest the body) attachment of the *Radius* and *Ulna* in the arm.	Rotation is the primary movement (eg when turning your arm over, the radius rotates to allow the palm to turn).
Saddle	Convex surface (rider) articulates with concave surface (saddle) of another bone.	The thumb: where the *Metacarpal* articulates with the *Trapezium* of the hand.	Movement in two planes: flexion and extension, and rotation.

- **Muscle Bulk** – This is demonstrated in some well-muscled performers who cannot bend their arms throughout the full range of movement because their biceps muscles get in the way and prevent full ROM. This must not be confused with the old wives' tale that the more muscle someone has, the less flexible they are. Many athletes have very large amounts of muscle and are very flexible.

- **Age** – Children are naturally more flexible than adults, although this ability is lost as the child grows towards puberty, unless it is maintained through training.

- **Gender** – Females tend to be naturally more flexible than males.

- **Activity Level** – The more active a person is, the greater the level of flexibility that they would tend to have.

However, the major limiting factor to ROM is the *elasticity* (the ability to return to resting length after being stretched) and the *plasticity* (tendency to take on a longer length after a stretch) of the muscle fibres, tendons and ligaments of a player. These factors can be positively altered by stretching and by working through a full range of movement when doing weight-training and other exercises.

The Importance of Stretching

Stretching is the training method that enables flexibility to be developed. Stretching can be used to improve both static and dynamic flexibility. *Static flexibility* relates to the range of movement possible in a passive movement (ie one that requires no direct muscular action). External forces, such as gravity, a partner, or a machine, provide the force that enables the stretch to take place. *Dynamic flexibility* relates to the range of joint movement possible during active movements. Dynamic and static stretching methods can be used to improve dynamic and static flexibility, but they also have different uses in the training routine.

Flexibility Training

Stretching is often associated with warming up and cooling down. While it is appropriate that different stretching methods are employed by coaches in preparation for, and immediately following, performance, this is not where flexibility is developed. As one of the fitness variables potentially influential to performance, flexibility should have training sessions devoted to its improvement, through regular stretching sessions that are performed for extended periods of 30–60 minutes.

It is during such times that flexibility is permanently increased, although it will be lost if this training is stopped or if the athlete does not continue to perform sport and conditioning skills through the full ranges of movement. As with all adaptations to training, the rule of *use it or lose it* applies. Recovery, and a further reduction in the incidence of injuries that may occur as the player undergoes a rigorous training routine, will be massively aided by such flexibility training sessions. If combined with imagery and visualisation training, and appropriate music, these sessions can be very beneficial for relaxation and refocusing. Such sessions are most successful if undertaken in a quiet room, with appropriate accompanying music and at the same time every day, following a routine developed by the individual. These sessions should last 25–30 minutes and should stretch all of the major muscles.

Developing a Stretching Routine

Stretching routines should start in the middle of the body to ensure that the major muscle groups are mobilised first, thereby allowing for greater potential flexibility in the smaller muscle groups. Therefore, the order of stretching in the routine should be:

- back (torso)
- hips (pelvic region)
- *hamstrings*
- groin
- *quadriceps*
- calves, ankles, feet
- shoulders
- arms, wrists
- neck.

Dynamic Stretching

A dynamic stretch usually involves rhythmic-type movements that may extend to full range. The term *dynamic flexibility* refers to the maximum ROM of a joint during a movement, or its ease of movement within the obtainable ROM. This method of stretching has sometimes been criticised as exceeding the elastic limit of the tissues as a result of the repetitive bouncing actions. However, dynamic (movement) stretches should prepare the muscles for the impending exercise by working rhythmically through sport-specific ranges of movements under direct muscular control, and should therefore work, and gradually increase, the elastic range of the tissues without causing acute over-reaching. As the drills below outline, these exercises include such activities as butt kicks and high-knee drills, and also movements that relate to the specific activities that will be undertaken in performing any sport-specific actions. For example, consider twisting movements, diagonal movements of the trunk and vertical and horizontal movements.

Dynamic stretches should be used in preparation for training and sports performance. At this time, dynamic methods help to increase muscle temperature, temporarily increase the plastic potential of the muscles and help the neurological activation of muscles that will be used in a performance. Stretches performed at this time should be turned into a creative routine that will mirror most types of activities within the game, such as running, turning, jumping, rotating, hitting and lunging. More forceful, explosive stretches (*ballistic stretches*) that utilise momentum and velocity, rather than muscular control, should also be undertaken in a warm-up following rhythmical dynamic work. Ballistic stretches have an important role in preparing for training/participation in sports. Indeed, if such ballistic actions are not practised at appropriate speeds, then injury may occur in performing explosive actions. Ballistic stretching, when undertaken, should only take place in a properly controlled environment and be progressively introduced when the individual is well warmed up, is fully aware of the dangers involved in the stretch and knows how to properly execute the movement.

So why is dynamic stretching advocated in performance preparation rather than the more traditionally used static stretches? This requires some physiological explanation. Explosive plyometric actions (see Chapters 2, 4 and 5) in the muscles occur as the stretch reflex (stretch–shortening) mechanism. This is a protective mechanism in the body, which initiates a strong reflex contraction when the stretch receptors in the muscle perceive that the rate of change in muscle fibre length is too rapid or too forceful. For example, when landing from a squat jump, the *Quadricep* muscles are stretched rapidly. The stretch receptors within the muscle sense this change and limit the rate of stretch by initiating a reflex concentric contraction (ie a shortening of fibre length). End-of-range static stretching, when held for any period of time, can switch this stretch reflex mechanism off. This is demonstrated in a static *Hamstring* stretch:

• Sit on the floor, with legs out straight in front of you.

• Keeping the head up (this helps to avoid curvature in the lumbar spine) and back straight throughout, reach down the legs with both hands until a comfortable end position is reached (you should feel a definite stretching sensation, but no pain).

• Hold this position for a count of 20 and then relax.

• Now try to stretch a little further. You should find that you are able to do so, because the mechanisms that inhibit the extent of the stretch in the muscle have been switched off.

As sports need a power base that relies on the stretch–shortening cycle to facilitate explosive movements, then the inhibition of the stretch reflex (the stretch–shortening cycle) mechanism is not desirable. This inhibition will not only have an acute and immediate effect, but there is also evidence to suggest that subsequent levels of power production can be reduced by up to 40% for a period of over an hour following static stretching.

The following dynamic stretches are therefore suggested in order to maximise the physiological potential of the player. Coaches will need to be aware that players may, initially, not be psychologically prepared for performance following a dynamic stretching routine, in the sense that they may not perceive that they have actually stretched the muscle at all. This is a normal response in players who have spent many years preparing for training and matches by undertaking a static stretching routine. Coaches need to overcome such concerns in the player by firstly, having an extended education phase, to familiarise the player with the concepts and movements involved in such a routine, and secondly, by initially allowing players time within the routine to evolve their own ideas about how best to maximise the benefit of such a routine.

Dynamic Stretching Exercises

All of the stretches described below are highly adaptive and can be modified to incorporate specific movements from individual sports or specific pieces of equipment, such as a ball or stick.

Trunk Rotations

Stand with feet shoulder-width apart and arms fully stretched above the head. From here, rotate the body around to the left (five rotations) and right (five rotations), keeping your arms straight so that your hands make big circles as you move.

Figure 225: Trunk rotations

Stars

Lie on your front with arms and legs spread out into a star shape. From here, raise your left arm and right leg as high as you can and wiggle them up and down through the full range of movement for 10 seconds. This should then be repeated for the opposite arm and leg combination.

After this has been repeated on each side, raise both arms and legs together, and then squeeze them together as tightly as possible for a count of 10 (Figure 227).

Figure 226: Stars top position

Figure 227: Squeeze position

Back Crucifixes

Lie on your front with legs outstretched, feet together and arms at 90° to the body (a crucifix position). Keeping your hands in the same place and your shoulders in contact with the ground, attempt to rotate your trunk to the rear, touching the left foot to the right hand (Figure 228). The coach should ensure that the player moves the foot to touch the hand, rather than moving the hand down to make the movement easier. You then return to the start position and repeat the stretch to the other side.

Figure 228: Back crucifix mid-position

Front Crucifixes

Lie on your back, in the crucifix position, with arms straight out to your side and legs together. Keeping your hands and shoulders in the same position, alternate between touching left foot to right hand and right foot to left hand.

Figure 229: Front crucifix mid-position

Knee Rolls

Lie on your back, with knees pulled tight into the chest and arms wrapped around the knees. From this position, rock backwards and forwards, increasing the range of movement with each roll.

Figure 230: Knee rolls

Disco 1

Stand tall, with feet shoulder-width apart and right arm extended to a position at 90° to your body. Keeping your arm straight out and fully extended, bring your left knee up to your right elbow and return the foot to the ground. Repeat to the left.

Figure 231: Disco 1 mid-position

Disco 2

Stand tall, with feet shoulder-width apart and right arm extended to a position at 90° to your body. Keeping the arm straight out and the leg straight, swing your left foot up to touch your right hand. The foot is then returned to the ground. Repeat to the left.

Figure 232: Disco 2 mid-position

Standing Hamstring Swings

Stand on one leg (holding on to another player or a static object for support, if needed), with the pelvis in a neutral position and head looking forward. Keeping the upper body stationary, swing the non-standing leg forwards and backwards, allowing momentum to gradually increase the range of the swinging motion and keeping the swinging leg straight at all times. Repeat drill to the opposite side.

Figure 233: Standing hamstring swings

Standing Groin Swings

Stand on one leg (holding on to a static object for support if needed), with the pelvis in a neutral position and head looking forward. Keeping the upper body stationary, the player swings the non-standing leg from side to side, across and away from the body, allowing momentum to gradually increase the range of the swinging motion, and keeping the swinging leg straight at all times. Repeat drill to the opposite side.

Figure 234: Standing groin swings

Hip Rotators

This can be performed as a walking exercise, in both a forwards and a backwards direction. Start with your hands resting behind your head, elbows pointing away from the body. Take a step forward with your left foot, then bring the right foot forwards so that the knee of the right foot is brought outwards and as high/as close to the right elbow as possible. This is achieved with a rotation movement of the hip joint – the step begins with the foot behind the player's body and ends with the foot in front of the player's body. Upon landing, make the same rotation movement with the left foot. After a number of repetitions, you should undertake the same movement in reverse, rotating each leg in turn from a position in front of the body, to one behind, at the end of the step.

Figure 235: Hip rotators

Sprint Pull-throughs

Stand on one leg (holding on to a static object for support if needed), with the pelvis in a neutral position and head looking forward. Lift your left leg to a high-knee position in front of the body by flexing both the hip and the knee (Figure 236), then, maintaining the height of the knee, extend the knee to a straight position (Figure 237), and then extend the hip so that the leg is pulled through underneath the body. The ball of your foot should contact the ground slightly behind the body.

Figure 236: Sprint pull-throughs – high-knee position

Figure 237: Sprint pull-throughs – foot-extended position

Figure 238: Sprint pull-throughs – moving-to-ground-contact position

Walking High-knee Grabs
Perform a forward and, later, a backward walking action, keeping the trunk upright and the head high. With each step, as you raise your knee, put your arms around your shins, and pull the knee as close to the trunk as possible (while keeping the trunk upright). This position is held briefly, then released, and the foot lands as you step forward. This action is then repeated with the other leg.

Figure 239: Walking high-knee grabs top position

Butt Kicks
This is a commonly used exercise for developing sprint technique. Move forward by flicking your heels up to touch the buttocks, contacting the floor with the balls of your foot. At the same time, drive your arms backwards and forwards from the shoulders in a sprint-arm action, with your elbows bent at 90° and hands moving from level with the hips to level with the chin.

Figure 240: Butt kicks

Lunges
The lunge is an exercise that can be adapted in a number of ways to incorporate different stretching actions. From a standing position, you deliberately flex the hip of the leg that will be leading the movement. The knee of this leg should also be flexed, both to an angle of 90°. Take an exaggerated step forwards with the lead leg, which is planted flat on the ground. Flex the lead knee, moving so that it is shifting along the same line that the toes of the lead foot are pointing to (Figure 241). At the same time, come onto the ball of your foot on the trail leg, and lower the knee of this leg to a bottom position that is approximately 3–5 centimetres off the floor. The trunk should be kept upright throughout the movement, with your centre of mass being directly above the mid-point between the two legs. You should alternate the lead leg with each stretch in order to ensure full benefits of the stretch.

Figure 241: Lunge

This exercise can be developed so that the lead leg is placed at a number of different angles (eg in Figure 242), allowing a range of fibres to be stretched. It is important for the player to ensure that the knee of the lead leg is flexed in a line that is the same as the toes of the foot of the lead leg. The movement can also be performed with a trunk rotation, so that the upper body is turned away from the lead leg at the bottom of the lunge position (Figure 243). At all times, the head should be held high and the chest facing upwards.

Figure 242: Angled lunge

Figure 243: Lunge with rotation

Squats

This is exactly the same exercise as performed in weight training. Your head should be up at all times, chest high and back straight. Your knees and hips should flex fully, dropping the buttocks as close to the floor as possible. Your feet should remain flat on the floor throughout the movement.

Figure 244: Squats

Kareoka

Turn sideways on to the direction of movement, with your arms extended at shoulder height and held at an angle that is 90° to your trunk. Take the front leg one step away from the rear leg. The rear leg (left leg in Figure 245) is then brought across in front of your body (with the knee as high as possible throughout the movement) to land as far away from the take-off position as possible. Your front/right leg is then moved across behind your body, so that you are in the same position as at the start (Figure 246). From here, take the left leg behind the body (with a dip of the left hip) and contact the ground as far away from the take-off point as possible (Figure 247), then move your right leg across. This sequence is repeated moving in one direction, and then repeated with the player facing the same way, but moving in the other direction. This means that the lead leg is reversed from the right to the left.

Figure 245: Kareoka first step **Figure 246: Kareoka second step** **Figure 247: Kareoka third step**

Shoulder Swings

This upper-body movement can be combined with a number of different movements, such as the lunges. Keep your trunk and head upright throughout the movement and rotate straight arms as close to your ears as possible in both a forwards and backwards direction.

Figure 248: Shoulder swings

Arm Throws

This is a two-phase stretch. Keeping the head up and the trunk upright, drive the arms backwards at shoulder height to open up the chest, leading with the elbows (Figure 249). Return your arms to the front of your body, keeping them at shoulder height, before driving them back again, this time straightening your arms and leading with the hands (Figure 250).

Figure 249: Arm throws elbows leading

Figure 250: Arm throws hands leading

Other exercises commonly used in dynamic flexibility routines include press-ups, twist sit-ups and a number of exercises commonly used within speed-technique drills, such as fast-feet, high-knees and skipping variations.

Static Stretching

Static or slow stretching is possibly the oldest and the most common technique in use. This involves taking a joint and its associated muscle group(s) to the end or near-end of range and holding the lengthened position as tension slowly decreases. Stretches should be held at the end position for a time period of between 15 and 40 seconds, with 2–4 reps completed per stretch. Lengthening a muscle to its end range of movement (ROM) and holding it there in a static stretch seems unlikely to produce injury to the soft tissue unless the muscle is overstretched or body positioning is incorrect.

Each stretch that is performed will have a defined beginning and end point. This end point (the position at which the stretch should be finished, or held in a static stretch) is the position at which the player feels a comfortable stretching sensation, but no sharp pains or cramps. If the player feels either of these symptoms, it means that they have overstretched, and the position should immediately be released. When stretching, the player should always exhale as they manoeuvre into the stretch.

There are a number of static stretches that can be performed for individual muscle groups, each of which has a number of variations. Those detailed below are considered to be easy, effective and safe methods of static stretching of the major muscle groups used in the majority of sports, although there are many variations of these that can be performed.

Back (Torso)

Lower Back

Lie flat on your back and bring your knees to your chest, with your feet as close to the buttocks as possible. The knees should be drawn towards the chest, as far as possible, by pulling with the arms *behind* the knees (this avoids hyperflexion of the knee joint). From this position, exhale and pull your knees towards your chest, raising the hips off the floor.

Figure 251: Lower-back static stretch

Abdominals and Trunk Stabilisers

Lie on your stomach, with elbows directly below the shoulders and palms flat on the floor (Figure 252). Keeping your hands still and the pelvis in contact with the floor, straighten the arms until they can go no further (Figure 253). Hold this position, then return to the floor.

Now reach the left arm around to the left side, keeping the pelvis in the same position and arms bent. Again, your arms are straightened so that your body twists to the left, and are held at the point when you cannot straighten your arm further without moving the pelvis (Figure 254). At this point, turn your head as far left as you can, to stretch the front neck muscles. Then return to the start position and repeat to the right.

Figure 252: Start position

Figure 253: Trunk-extended position

Figure 254: Trunk extended and rotated

Upper Back

Begin by kneeling on both knees, so that there is a 90° angle at the knees and the trunk is upright. Raise both arms straight up in the air, as high as possible (Figure 255). From here, lean forward as far as possible, so that the trunk and shoulders are fully extended and the palms of your hands are flat on the floor (Figure 256). From this position, exhale and sit back on your ankles, keeping your hands in the same position on the ground (Figure 257). The stretch should be felt throughout the shoulders and the muscles of the upper back.

Figure 255: Kneeling in the start position **Figure 256: Fall in to the trunk position** **Figure 257: Sitting back on to the ankles**

Gluteals and *Abductors*

Sit on the floor with your legs extended and hands slightly behind them supporting the torso. From here, cross your left foot over your right leg and slide the heel towards the buttocks as far as possible (keeping your foot flat on the floor). Rotate the trunk to the left as far as possible (look over your left shoulder), and place your right elbow on the outside of your left knee (Figure 258). From here, exhale and look over your left shoulder while rotating the trunk and gently push on your left knee with the right elbow, pushing the leg towards the right. Hold this position, then return to the start position and repeat on the other side.

Figure 258: Gluteal and *Abductor* stretch

Hamstring and *Hip Flexor* Combination Stretches

This sub-routine stretches the *Hamstring* and *Gluteals*, and the *Hip flexors*, including *Iliopsoas*, *Quadriceps* and *Abdominals*.

Phase 1

Kneel on your left knee, with trunk upright. Extend your right leg so that the bend at the knee is greater than 90° (but the knee is not straight – this allows the belly of the muscle, rather than the ends, to be stretched). Point the toes of your right foot towards the floor, and turn slightly inwards at the ankle. Keep your head up and the trunk straight at all times (a rounding of the back will change the stretch from a *Hamstring* stretch into a back stretch), and bend forward from the waist (about the lower pelvis), bringing your head as close to your knee as is comfortably possible (Figure 259). Hold this position before returning to the start position.

Phase 2

Return to the start position (kneeling on left knee), and raise your left arm straight above your head (or right arm if the left leg is forward). Maintain an upright position, extending the trunk while keeping your left knee anchored to the floor. From here, the pelvis is pushed forward (with no pelvic tilt) to a comfortable end position, then hold (see Figure 260).

You then return to the start position of Phase 1 and extend the right leg further in front. This sequence is repeated 2–3 times for each leg.

The players have to make sure the knees and, especially, the feet do not roll inward – the coach should watch for any movement from the centre line. In some individuals, placing a towel or mat under the left knee prevents any soreness to the patella. In Phase 2, the coach should watch for any tilting movements of the pelvis. Ensure the extended knee is kept bent in a wide angle and the hip and trunk are extended in order to stretch *Iliopsoas*.

Figure 259: *Hamstring* stretch   **Figure 260: *Hip flexor* stretch**

***Hamstring* and Groin Complex**

This stretches the *Adductors* in the groin and the *Hamstrings* at the back of the leg.

Sit on the floor, with your legs out straight in front of you. From this position, bend your left leg out to the side, and place the sole of your left foot against the inner surface of your right thigh (Figure 261). Keeping the head up (this helps to avoid curvature in the lumbar spine), reach down your right leg with both hands until a comfortable end position is reached. Hold this position for the appropriate count (15–30 seconds) and then relax.

The legs should then be *shaken off* and the stretch repeated with the end point pushed a little further down the leg. Repeat three times for each leg. The head should be kept up and back straight throughout the movement. The coach should ensure that the player avoids any bouncing or excessive reaching along the extended leg. If possible, the player should pull the toes of the extended leg towards the body, as this allows a player to obtain further stretch to the calf muscles.

Figure 261: *Hamstring* and groin complex stretch

Quadriceps and *Hip Flexor* Stretch

Kneel on your right knee, with your left foot flat on the floor in front of the knee. Lean forward, so that there is a diagonal line formed between your right thigh and shoulders. You should keep your back as flat as possible. Keeping the knee and foot positions as they are, bend the lower part of your right leg up, and catch your toes (or as much of the foot as possible) with your left hand. Pull the lower leg up (towards the buttocks) and across (towards the left) until the end point of the stretch (comfortable stretching sensation) is reached. The stretch should then be repeated with the leg positions reversed.

Figure 262: *Quadriceps* and hip flexor stretch

Quadriceps

Stand on your left leg, holding on to a wall or other support. Bending the right knee and grasping the ankle from behind with your *left* hand, slightly bend the standing (left) leg and pull the ankle of the bent leg towards the buttocks, keeping the knees together and the pelvis in a neutral position. This should be repeated twice for each leg.

**Figure 263: Standing *Quadriceps*
stretch – second phase**

The next phase of the stretch involves standing on your left leg holding on to a wall or other support. Your right knee is bent and grasped at the ankle from behind with your *right* hand. The stretching action is then repeated.

The coach should make sure that the player does not allow the knee to drift outward. Players should also try to avoid leaning forward or tilting the pelvis, which will increase the lumbar curve in the spine. The spine should be kept as normally straight as possible and, as the leg is pulled back, the *Abdominals* should be contracted to ensure that the stretch is lengthened through the knee.

Groin

Lower yourself into a deep squat position, with feet flat on the floor and wider than shoulder-width apart. Your toes should be turned slightly outwards, and the buttocks should be as close to your ankles as possible. From here, place the palms of your hand flat on the ground, inside the knees, with the elbows resting against the thighs. Exhale and lean forward slightly, pushing outwards with the elbows until a comfortable end point is reached. Using the elbows to provide manual resistance (by pushing them outwards), this can be easily utilised as a proprioceptive neuromuscular facilitation (PNF) stretch (see page 155).

Figure 264: Groin stretch

Crucifix

Figure 265: Crucifix

Lie on your back, in the crucifix position, with arms straight out to your sides and legs together. Keeping your hands and shoulders in the same position, move your left leg to touch your right hand and hold. Relax and repeat the other side.

Calves

Stand facing a wall (or other similar support) using the arms for stability. Stand with your right leg in a back position, keeping your knee straight, foot flat and at right angles to the wall, with the heel down (Figure 266). This stretches the *Gastrocnemius* (larger calf muscle). After holding, repeat the same stretch, but bend your knee. This targets the *Soleus* (smaller, deeper calf muscle) (Figure 267). The opposite forward leg is relaxed and slightly bent. After positioning your feet, you should lean forward, bending the elbows and keeping the hips in line with the shoulders. This should increase dorsiflexion (toe pulled towards knee) of the rear ankle. The coach should pay particular attention to the heel and hip position, and make sure that the player's weight is pushed forward and downward.

Figure 266: The straight-leg *Gastrocnemius* stretch

Figure 267: Bent-leg *Soleus* stretch

Achilles Tendon

Kneeling on both knees, with the buttocks resting on the ankles, raise your right knee, so that the foot comes forward into a position where the instep of the foot is next to the left knee, with the foot remaining flat on the floor. Exhale and lean forwards, pushing the knee forward and simultaneously sinking your body weight back onto your ankles (dropping the bottom towards the heel). The foot must be kept flat on the floor at all times if the player is to feel a stretching sensation in the achilles tendon and lower calf muscle.

Figure 268: Achilles tendon stretch

Chest

Stand in a doorway, at an external corner, or use a partner standing behind you and use this as a foundation to support your arm, just inside the elbows, which should be flexed to 90°. Keep your elbow at shoulder height, with forearm pointing straight upward and held flat against the walls or doorway. From here, exhale and lean forward so that the arm is supporting your body weight. This will particularly stretch the *Sternal* and shoulder insertions of the *Pectoral* muscles, which are vital in many pushing and ripping motions in sports.

Figure 269: Chest stretch front view   **Figure 270: Chest stretch rear view**

Shoulders

Sit or stand and move one arm across in front of your body, keeping the palm facing forward and your arm at shoulder height. Bend your other hand underneath this arm, at a position slightly above the elbow and, as you exhale, pull the elbow across the body, while keeping the trunk facing forward. After holding at the appropriate point, repeat the stretch with your arm rotated so that the palm faces towards the body.

Figure 271: Palm facing away from the body

Figure 272: Palm facing towards the body

Triceps and *Latissimus Dorsi* (Lats) – Back

Stand with one arm raised overhead, as close to your ear as possible and flexed at the elbow, so that your hand is resting behind you, on the opposite shoulder blade. With the other hand, grasp the outside of the flexed elbow, exhale and pull the elbow behind your head to an appropriate hold position. The coach must ensure that the trunk is kept upright throughout the stretch.

Figure 273: Stretching the Lats and *Triceps*

Trapezius (Upper Back) and Neck

Stand with your feet shoulder-width apart and reach your left hand across your back (with the palm facing away from the body). Reach across the body, so that you can hold your left wrist with your right hand. Keep looking forward and without raising your right shoulder, tilt your head as if trying to touch your right ear to your right shoulder. This should be held at the appropriate position, then relaxed and repeated with the right hand behind you.

Figure 274:*Trapezius* stretch

Proprioceptive Neuromuscular Facilitation Stretching

This form of stretch typically involves a partner, although there are ways to do proprioceptive neuromuscular facilitation (PNF) stretching without one. While there are a number of different PNF techniques currently in use, a sensible one to use is the contract–relax (CR) method. This involves taking a muscle to a comfortable end-of-range position (assisted by a partner or manual resistance), actively contracting the muscle, then relaxing the muscle. As the muscle is relaxed, the end-of-range position is increased until a newer, comfortable end position is reached. This sequence of contract-relax-stretch should be continued four times per muscle group, with the first 20-second contraction being at 50% maximum, the second at 60%, the third at 75% and the final position should be held by the partner (or whatever manual resistance is being employed), with no active muscular contraction.

For example, a *Hamstring* stretch (see Figure 275). The muscle is first taken to its lengthened end-of-range position. The player pushes against the partner's resistance to produce a 50% contraction in the *Hamstring* muscles (50% attempt to move the leg toward the floor during the push phase) as the partner opposes the contraction. This position is held for 20 seconds, at which time the *Hamstring* muscles relax while the partner increases passive pressure to further increase the ROM. The sequence is then repeated three times, as described above.

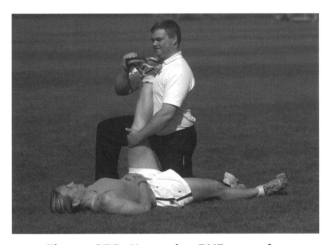

Figure 275: *Hamstring* PNF stretch

This type of stretching also helps to develop strength throughout the range of joint motion. However, it should only be used when the coach has experience of the technique and the player is able to understand how to communicate when an end position has been reached and is also able to control muscular contractions of differing strengths. PNF stretching can also leave a player with some slight delayed onset of muscular soreness (DOMS), caused by micro-traumas that can develop within the muscle fibres. Coaches should therefore take care with the use of PNF within the overall training programme if the techniques are to be used effectively.

Summary

- Flexibility refers to the range of movement possible around a joint. It is a beneficial quality for players to have, because the greater the range of movement a player has, the more options for performing a skill they will be able to carry out.

- The best ways to improve flexibility are to train through a full range of movement and utilise flexibility-training sessions as part of the training programme.

- Dynamic stretching movements are highly adaptive to sporting demands and should be used by coaches in the preparation for performance (during the period traditionally known as the *warm-up*).

- Static stretching should not be used as part of a warm-up (ie prior to training or playing) as it could be detrimental to the player's ability to produce power. Static stretching is ideal for use in cool-downs (following training and playing) and in flexibility-training sessions. Care should be taken not to overstretch at this stage, as this will cause increased muscle fibre damage.

- Static stretches should be taken to a comfortable end-of-range position (where the player feels a comfortable stretching sensation but no pain) and held for 20–30 seconds before being released.

Further Reading

Alter, M.J. (2005) *Sport Stretch*. Illinois: Human Kinetics. ISBN: 0-880118-23-7.

Pearson, A. (2003) *Dynamic Flexibility*. A & C Black. ISBN: 0-713664-52-5.*

* Available from Coachwise 1st4sport. For a full range of sports education and training equipment, please visit www.1st4sport.com or call 0113-201 5555.

Chapter 8
Recovery Training for Optimal Performance

Introduction

For coaches of all levels, whether working with full-time players who train every day, semi-professional performers who train together twice a week but undertake their own fitness work, or amateur athletes who train once or twice a week, it is still important to have players who are training and performing at optimum capability. Much of the emphasis on training relates to maximising the physical, psychological, technical, tactical and environmental variables that underpin performance. However, the model for ongoing best performance is derived from the following equation:

Optimal Work in Training/Performance + Optimal Recovery from Training/Match = Best Performance

How many coaches can say that they put as much emphasis on their performer's recovery as they do the training? In any environment that involves multiple training and playing scenarios, whether with adult players, children in schools or competing on a competitive schedule, there is a need to facilitate an active recovery programme into the performers' schedule. The aim of this chapter is to introduce some practical mechanisms that coaches may wish to utilise in their routines, in order to achieve optimal recovery.

Short-term Consequences of Training

Assuming the player does not train too hard/heavily[29] in a session, the most common consequence of training is muscle soreness. Delayed onset of muscle soreness (DOMS) – also known as *induced muscle damage* – is experienced. As the latter name suggests, this is caused by microscopic muscle damage and is associated with symptoms such as swelling, soreness and restricted range of motion[30] for up to 48 hours. There is also a significant drop-off in performance capacity – often for up to four days when there is no aided recovery – with players typically reporting a lower daily self-rating of wellness the day after a game. This four-day period is also associated with a higher incidence of cough and cold symptoms.

Long-term Consequences of Overtraining/Under-recovery

If a player progressively trains when they have not appropriately recovered from a bout of previous training (Figure 276), the player is liable to develop symptoms associated with overtraining/under-recovery syndrome. The theory underpinning the appropriate time to train is explained in the overcompensation cycle model section on page 171.

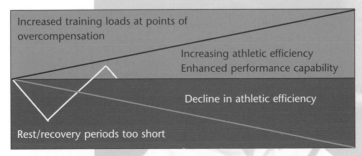

Increased training loads at points of overcompensation

Increasing athletic efficiency
Enhanced performance capability

Decline in athletic efficiency

Rest/recovery periods too short

Figure 276: Cumulative effects of training

The symptoms associated with overtraining are multi-faceted and sometimes contradictory. For example, many players report an accelerated resting heart rate, while others experience the opposite – a suppressed resting heart rate. One of the most obvious indicators is an unexplained decrease in performance, which is often problematic, as the coach's remedy for this is often to make the performer train harder, making the problem worse. Other common physical indicators include, a sudden loss in body mass and a loss of appetite or change in eating habits. Sleep patterns can also become disrupted, with players either not getting sufficient sleep because the player experiences disturbed sleep or, conversely, the player's sleeping time far exceeds the normal requirement[31].

The coach can also look for signs and symptoms when dealing directly with players. Often, overtrained players will complain that their legs feel tired, heavy or sore, or that they do not feel good (although the coach must know the players well enough to make sure that this is not a sign of the player being lazy or simply moaning, as performers sometimes like to do!). An athlete's body language can also be observed to indicate cumulative fatigue. A slumped posture about the shoulders, languid facial expression and pale colouring, *washed-out* eye colouring, bending over to recover from efforts and unexplained bad technique may all be indicators of cumulative fatigue. However, these may be indicators of other psychosocial problems as well, so again, the coach needs to know the players well.

Psychological indicators are also important. As mentioned previously, look for low motivation levels in previously well-motivated players, poor concentration, a lack of self-confidence and unexplained levels of aggression. Performers may also experience increases in the number of colds, coughs and other illnesses, due to suppression of the immune system resulting from excessive stress, and/or overuse injuries caused by excessive or maladapted biomechanical loading.

Monitoring Training Status

As a general practice, players have been encouraged to keep training diaries for a number of years now. These are invaluable aids in recording and monitoring training progress and providing data that can be used to set goals. Wellness diaries work on a similar principle. These diaries are simply designed to record the variables closely associated with under-recovery, that is, workload, resting heart rate, body mass, sleep patterns, nutritional status and attitude towards/energy for training. While this seems like a lot of data for a performer to collect on a daily basis, the diaries can range from very detailed records to very simple and easy-to-complete sheets that use Likert scales[32] for straightforwardness. Table 7 shows some example variables and typical Likert scales of response.

Table 7: Example data categories for a wellness diary

Variable	Example Measurement
Workload	*Heavy/moderate/light*
Resting heart rate	*Insert recorded figure (bpm)*
Body mass	*Insert recorded figure (kg)*
Sleep	*No. of hours: excellent/good/average/poor*
Daily nutrition	*Excellent/good/average/poor*
Attitude to training/energy for training	☺ ☻ ☹

For example, feeling tired the day after a game or tournament is understandable, but if a player feels lethargic for several days, this may be indicative of a problem. Similarly, while recording body mass will not indicate the body composition of the player, a sudden drop in body mass (ie more than 4%) may indicate a potential problem.

Body mass should be recorded after rising and going to the toilet in the morning, but before breakfast. Resting pulse should be taken a couple of minutes after waking (assuming that you are not awoken with a start) and prior to rising. Differences of more than 20% above normal are indicative of a potential problem. A combination of sustained increased resting heart rate and loss of body mass should be investigated by the coach, to ascertain the state of the player.

Post-performance Recovery

As soon as the final whistle goes in a match or training session, the player should begin the recovery process. The initial phase becomes the post-event cool-down. This is the hardest part of the session for the coach to enforce, as the interesting part of the day has now been completed and many players now want to unwind and enjoy things away from the pitch.

There have been many recommended guidelines on how to structure a cool-down and how long it should last for. As a minimum, players need to walk or move lightly for 4–5 minutes after the game, followed by a period of stretching the major muscles while they are warm. The walking helps to alleviate blood pooling: during exercise, the heart is aided in pumping the blood to the working muscles and back to the heart by the muscular actions in the legs creating a pumping effect. Upon cessation of exercise, this pumping mechanism ceases, often resulting in a volume of blood pooling in the legs. This can cause a player to feel dizzy and possibly faint, due to a lack of blood in the head. Blood pooling also prevents the effective removal of metabolic waste products from the muscles that have been working in training.

Static stretching (refer to guidelines in Chapter 7) at this time should be restricted to the major muscles of the body, although this should not necessarily be taken to the end-of-range position, as this may induce further micro-tears to the muscle. The benefits of stretching immediately after performing are that it allows the muscle tension to be decreased and also increases the speed of neural innervations to the muscles, thus allowing the recovery process to be hastened further.

Too much emphasis should not be placed on stretching at this time, however, as this will have little benefit to the player in the long term and will almost certainly not be carried out with the necessary discipline, due to the player's frame of mind. There is a perpetuated myth that cool-down stretches are an ideal time to permanently increase the length of the muscles, as they are being stretched when the muscle is at its most elastic. However, there is much evidence to support an argument against this, due to the small amount of time that a player will effectively spend stretching in this period. More appropriately, the player should undertake flexibility-training sessions during the week to achieve this aim, as discussed in Chapter 7.

Contrast Bathing

We are all familiar with the *energised/bracing* feeling that we have when we go from a warm environment into a very cold one. This is due to the brain having to recognise and respond to signals from two sources of information (ie the hot and the cold), resulting in the increased feeling of stimulation. Contrast bathing works on a very similar principle (with continuous alteration between the temperature extremes) and can be achieved through the use of either a shower or a spa and plunge pool arrangement. This treatment also serves to increase blood flow to the worked muscles and is therefore beneficial in removing the metabolic by-products of exercise, thus allowing players to recover more quickly from high-intensity training.

The other benefit of this form of regeneration is that it requires a minimum amount of time, using facilities that are readily available in any sports club, training facility or hotel tour venue. After showering the skin clean, players should step into a warm (35–37°C) shower or spa/bath for 2 minutes or 4 minutes respectively. Pressure from high water jets and power-shower nozzles has been demonstrated to aid muscle relaxation and considerably reduce DOMS in players. The temptation to stay in the warm environment must, however, be avoided, as this can offset the benefits of the treatment and possibly lead to dehydration and neural fatigue. After the appropriate time, the player should then enter a cold (10–14°C) shower for 20–30 seconds or bath/plunge pool for 30–60 seconds, before returning to the warm environment. This process should be repeated three times for optimal efficiency. If the club does not have cold showers or a plunge pool, the same effect can easily be achieved by filling a portable paddling pool or a wheelie-bin with iced water for the players to immerse themselves in.

Re-hydration

Water is essential to normal body function and elite players should be drinking more than 4 litres of fluid every day. Research has indicated that 5% dehydration can lead to a performance decrement of up to 20%. During exercise, the major cause of water loss from the body is through sweat. If a coach is unsure how much water a performer can lose during a training session (which will obviously be influenced by environmental conditions), they should weigh their athletes before and after training (remembering to remove wet and sweaty clothing). One kilogram lost equates to 1 litre of fluid that must be replaced with water as quickly as possible after the game. However, the player must be careful to avoid drinking too much, too quickly to replace fluid lost, as they can rapidly develop hyponatraemia – an over-dilution of the blood sodium levels – and this causes the player to become water intoxicated (eg one player who suffered from this drank 6 litres in 1 hour). The condition only rights itself, given a normally functioning kidney, after several unpleasant hours.

Water lost through sweat must be replaced, both during and immediately after matches and training, and players should be practised in both. Indeed, during performances, keeping hydrated is more important than supplying fuel to the muscles. Careful consideration should be given to the drink that coaches supply to players during training. Drinks that are too concentrated will slow the process of water absorption from the gut into the body, and will consequently contribute to any dehydration effect. The drink should be diluted to between 4 and 6 millilitres of glucose/maltodextrin/electrolyte per 100 millilitres of water. If the coach is unsure of the concentration of a sports drink, remember that water is a much better option than a cordial that is mixed too strongly. Following a game, drinking high-energy drinks containing glucose, sucrose or maltodextrins in concentrations of 6 millilitres:100 millilitres can help to achieve both the rehydration and carbohydrate replenishment needs of the player.

It should be realised that the body's warning mechanism of dehydration is the feeling of thirst. Please note that this means that you are *already* dehydrated and have not been drinking enough. Prevention is, however, better than cure, and so ongoing monitoring of hydrated status is necessary. A good indicator of a player's hydration status is the urine: it should be clear and odourless, and passed every couple of hours.

Refuelling

Coaches should also ensure that, during this period immediately following exercise, players are not only rehydrated, but also that the muscle glycogen stores (the muscle carbohydrate energy supply), which become depleted by exercise, are re-stocked. Following intense exercise, there is a window of up to 2 hours when the body is optimally adjusted to replenish muscular glycogen stores. For this reason, players should aim to have 1 gram of carbohydrate per kilogram body mass (or at least 50 grams, eg two large bananas) during this time period. The same should be consumed for every subsequent 2-hour period, until a full meal is eaten. Proteins should also be consumed at this time, to aid the rebuilding process in the muscles.

Alcohol

Many games players have traditionally enjoyed an alcoholic drink after performing. However, alcohol delays the recovery process significantly. Firstly, it promotes dehydration, as it suppresses the secretion of anti-diuretic hormone, resulting in an increased volume of urine production, leaving blood plasma volume significantly decreased. Secondly, alcohol has a depressive effect on central nervous system activity, dulling the pain sensation from any injuries picked up during a previous game[33]. The depressant effect on the neurological stimulation to the muscle, coupled with the effect of dehydration upon the muscle cells, means that alcohol can retard the recovery process at a significant rate. A general rule for a player to follow is to drink alcohol in moderation and to not have any alcohol until rehydrated enough to urinate following the game.

It should be remembered that excess alcohol has secondary effects that will also not be conducive to optimal recovery, such as poor or disturbed sleep, impaired immune function through developed fatigue, or maybe even psychological disturbances relating to anxiety from memory loss.

Regeneration the Day After the Game

Swimming Pool Regeneration

The use of water as a healing medium can be traced as far back as 2400 BC in the proto-Indian culture. This is supported by much scientific evidence relating to the physical properties and fluid dynamics of water. When a body is fully or partially immersed in water, it experiences an upward thrust equal to the weight of the water displaced. This means that many activities, such as running, can be undertaken in water while not being subject to impact loading caused by ground reactions forces. There is also an accrued psychological benefit, as the feeling of weightlessness associated with suspension in the water can be linked to psychological relaxation strategies, such as visualisation, to enhance the regeneration effect. Hydrostatic pressure is also exerted equally on all surfaces of an immobilised object and this pressure increases with the depth of the water. For example, if an individual is standing in a 4-foot deep pool, the pressure of the water at their foot would be roughly four times greater than the pressure at the surface. This pressure would be approximately double that exerted by a standard elastic bandage, and so it not only helps to reduce swelling and fluid gathering at the site of injuries, but also has a massaging effect on the immersed muscles.

Table 8 details an example of a swimming pool regeneration session for use with players the day after a match. This is designed to keep the players moving and to stretch all of the major muscles and joints during a 15-minute session in a pool without a depth gradient (1.2 metres is a standard for such pools).

Aqua-jogging belts, which fit around the waist and enable the player to remain upright and run/walk around in deep water, are ideal for use in regeneration sessions in deeper water, where activities such as jogging, arms-only punching and treading water could all be utilised in an aided capacity. The number of activities that could be introduced into such sessions is limitless. It is often beneficial to use such training sessions for other purposes, such as team-building exercises or fun activities (eg aqua-aerobics or relay-running events) that provide a distraction from the routines of training but also ensure that the players have a regeneration session in the pool. Such sessions become particularly important during tournaments, or on tour, when the need for pool and regeneration work is great but the sessions need constant variety in order to maintain the players' interest.

Table 8: Example of a pool session designed to facilitate recovery between training sessions

Exercise	Duration (Seconds)	Notes
Slow walking (backwards and forwards)	60	–
Loose-arms skipping and jumping	60	–
Hip rotators forwards*	60	Hands on head, bring knees up to touch elbows and land foot in front of body. Repeat with other leg. Pelvis to remain neutral throughout. A slow movement to emphasise stretch.
Hip rotators backwards*	60	Pelvis to remain neutral throughout. A slow movement to emphasise stretch.
Jogging (backwards and forwards)	60	–
Straight-leg swings: front–back	2 x 30 each leg	Maintain an upright trunk. Hold partner or poolside for support.
On back, breaststroke legs	60	Arms loose by the side
Breaststroke, arms only	60	Leg buoy will aid body position in water.
Front crawl at 70% pace	60	–
Backstroke, arms only	60	Full stretch of shoulders and full range of motion.
Backstroke, legs only	60	Straight-leg kick from the hip.
Push and glide	3 reps	Glide through water as far as possible. Feel tension leaving body.
Star float	60	Switch off from session.

*see page 141

Power Naps

Everyone has a daily biorhythm (body clock) that is regulated by a number of things, including the chemical *melatonin*. This chemical reinforces the drive to sleep in a human being. Everyone has experienced times during the day when our body clock makes us feel sleepy, and there are many events in a player's week, such as a heavy training schedule, or lots of travelling, that can affect this body clock. Power naps (10–15 minutes) are an ideal way to quickly recharge the batteries and reset the body clock of the player during such times. They should not last any longer than 15 minutes, however, as this can result in an increased level of melatonin, with the knock-on effect that the player's afternoon activities and normal night-time sleep patterns may be disrupted.

Relaxation Technique

Psychological Relaxation

To try to separate psychological relaxation techniques from other regeneration methods is something of a *faux pas*, as these techniques are often best employed in conjunction with other active techniques – for example, during stretching routines. However, such techniques are often, as with most skills, initially best learned in isolation and progressively integrated into training as the player becomes more adept at the skill. Such techniques are excellent ways of controlling the anxieties and pressures that build up in a performer in the competitive environment. These techniques can either be *body to mind* (usually used when the symptoms are of a physical nature) or *mind to body*, which are usually used when the symptoms are manifested cognitively.

Relaxation, as with all mental skills, is something that needs to be practised and worked at. Relaxing in a silent room in your own home is very different from relaxing in the face of competition. The player needs to be able to make the transition from one environment to the other if they are to attain immediate activation control in any environment. The most basic body-to-mind technique is known as *progressive muscular relaxation*. This involves maximally tensing a muscle group and then focusing on maximally relaxing that muscle. This will enable the performer to distinguish between tension and relaxation in a given muscle. They should learn to be able to do this in a relaxed environment, but also progressively, under increased environmental stresses. Ultimately, the aim is to be able to quickly scan the muscles of the body to identify areas of undue tension in those muscles important for impending performance and to quickly focus on relaxing those individual muscles in the middle of the game. For example, scanning the body for those muscles important in kicking and relaxing those that are tense prior to place kicking in rugby, serving in tennis or taking a free throw in basketball.

Breathing techniques are also beneficial. Players should take a deep breath in through the nose, for a slow count of five, and then completely exhale through the mouth, to a slow count of eight. As the player becomes familiar with the timing, they should repeat the mantra *relax* as they inhale and exhale, feeling the tension leaving their body as they do this. Once a player is able to do this in a quiet environment, they should practise relaxing under conditions/in environments that are progressively more stressful.

Cognitive relaxation techniques normally utilise the skill of imagery. Imagery, or visualisation, is a psychological skill that must be progressively developed from simple beginnings to advanced levels, but it is not purely about the athlete *seeing* pictures of performances in their heads. It should be a polysensory experience (utilising all the senses), where performers can see what is occurring, hear the noises as they would expect to be around them, sense the environment, smell the smells, feel the same sensations/emotions as they would do if they were actually in the place they were picturing. The basic images to visualise are those that invoke a feeling of warmth and heaviness within the body, effortless actions, repetitive and relaxing sounds, etc. Good examples include lying on a beach, in the warm sand, feeling the sun on the back, listening to the repetitive sound of the waves lapping onto the shore.

Most meditation techniques have a basis in such imagery. However, in order for such techniques to be effective, players need to be in a comfortable position, in a warm and relaxed environment, and they have to have a passive attitude, which will allow thoughts to flow through the mind freely. Coupled with music and a comfortable environment, such relaxation techniques are ideal ways to end the day before going to bed, allowing the player to switch off from the pressures of the day and encourage restful sleep. This is important, as sleepless nights are definitely detrimental to efficient regeneration.

Relaxation Guidelines

Key Points Before Starting Relaxation

- Get into as comfortable a position as possible. Generally, it helps to loosen any tight clothing and keep your arms and legs slightly bent, not crossed or straight.

- Adjust the lighting in the room so that it is comfortable. Usually, relaxation works best in dark or dimly lit rooms.

- If anything about the relaxation process makes you uncomfortable, either physically or mentally, eliminate that component from your relaxation routine.

- When tensing your muscles, remember to inhale deeply and slowly (4–5 seconds). When you exhale say the word, 'calm' or 'relax' to yourself and relax completely. Over time, you will begin to associate the word you choose with the feeling of relaxation.

- Concentrate on the difference between tension and relaxation. Ensure that you spend approximately twice as much time relaxing each muscle group as the time spent tensing them.

The Relaxation Process

- Get yourself into a comfortable position – ie on the floor, a couch, bed, etc and close your eyes.

- Concentrate on your breathing – inhale slowly (for 4–5 secs) through your nose 20 times. Exhale slowly through the mouth.

- When you exhale, think of your cue word (eg *calm* or *relax*).

- Start by contracting your face muscles. Squinting and biting down hard with your teeth will help you to do this. Remember to inhale deeply. Then relax and repeat your cue word to yourself. Repeat this 3 times.

- Next, contract your neck muscles by making your neck as long as it will go. Remember to inhale deeply when you do this. Hold for 4–5 secs and then relax, repeating your cue word to yourself. Repeat this 3 times.

- Contract your shoulder muscles (raise shoulders) on an inhalation. Relax by lowering your shoulders on an exhalation. Remember to repeat your cue word. Repeat this 3 times.

- Make 2 fists on inhaling, relax on exhaling. Repeat this 3 times.

- Contract your finger muscles (spread the fingers) on inhaling, relax on exhaling. Repeat this 3 times.

- Contract your stomach muscles on inhaling, relax on exhaling. Repeat this 3 times.

- Contract your *Quadriceps* muscles on inhaling, relax on exhaling. Repeat this 3 times.

- Contract your calf muscles (point the toes towards your head) on inhaling, relax on exhaling. Repeat this 3 times.

- Contract your feet (push the toes forward) on inhaling, relax on exhaling. Repeat this 3 times.

- Concentrate on breathing again. Inhaling and exhaling 5–7 times.

- Visualise a staircase with 5–10 steps.

- Go down each step, one step at a time, getting more relaxed the further down the staircase you go.

- When you reach the bottom of the stairs, visualise the most comfortable place for you – specific, detailed, vivid images are important. What are you doing? Who is there? What colours do you see? What do you hear? What do you smell? Take some time to build and enjoy this scene.

- When you are comfortable, visualise yourself being successful (practising shots or during a match).

- Relax in your scene for 2–3 mins – remember to concentrate on your breathing.

- When you are ready, begin to climb the staircase slowly. When you reach the top, open your eyes slowly.

- With your eyes open, concentrate on your breathing 5 more times.

- Start to move your limbs slowly.

Stretching-training Sessions

Flexibility training (specific sessions built around stretching routines) should be performed at least every other day in a games player who is training 2–4 times per week. It is during such times that flexibility is permanently increased (although it will be lost if you stop this training), rather than during the warm-up (where dynamic stretches should be performed) and cool-down, as commonly thought. The benefits of stretching-training sessions are well documented and include decreased muscular tension, improved body-position awareness, decreased risk of injury problems occurring with antagonistic (opposite) and synergistic (assistor) muscle pairs. If combined with imagery and visualisation training and relaxing music, these sessions can be very beneficial for relaxation and refocusing. Such sessions (which should last for 20–30 minutes) are most successful if undertaken in a quiet room, with appropriate accompanying music (obviously the choice of the individual), and at the same time every day.

Massage

Many sports performers are realising the benefits of employing a consultant masseur to work on them during a training week. This is because massage can be used for the general relaxation of the musculo-skeletal system and is recognised as the best treatment for muscle tension, which develops as either an acute effect from over-reaching in a session or a chronic/cumulative side-effect of daily training. Massage also has the distinct advantage over many therapies in that, as well as being a general remedy, the treatment can also be directed into specific, local problem areas, thereby improving recovery. Indeed, with specific injuries, the skilled practitioner can explore the soft tissue more intimately than in any other therapy and problems can be diagnosed and treated very accurately. Massage is also a very adaptable regeneration aid, with treatments and techniques uniquely adapted to the specific needs of a player at any given time. For example, fractioning techniques have warming effects that are beneficial to the pliability of the soft tissues and improve cell metabolism; jostling/shaking techniques have been demonstrated to benefit the peripheral nervous system; deep-tissue fractioning can be used to break down the scar tissue that develops within muscles as a result of repetitive microtrauma, and deep massage has a pumping effect on the blood within the veins and arteries, improving the microcirculation within the treated muscle. Other benefits include improved tissue elasticity, pain reduction through the removal of metabolic by-products, the release of endorphins and increased tissue permeability of the muscle-cell membranes to oxygen-saturated fluids. When the massage treatment is applied to a large area of the body, there is also a substantial psychological benefit in terms of general relaxation and this is associated with improved sleep patterns and reduced psychological and physical stress.

Summary

- Actively promoting the recovery of a player following a game or training session is vital in order to ensure that they are playing and training with optimal intensity. This principle should apply whether a player is an amateur, semi-professional or full-time player. The heavier the training commitment that a player of any age has, the more important the recovery strategy becomes.

- The monitoring of training load and the effects of training is a key skill that the coach should work with their performer to develop. Wellness diaries are a simple and effective tool for this.

- Nutrition and rehydration are components that underpin the maintenance of a player's performance status.

- Swimming pool work, static stretching and massage therapy are all methods that a coach can employ to aid the player's recovery. Variation in the programme is something that the coach should consider in order to keep players motivated and interested in the developing programme.

- Psychological relaxation techniques should be learned in isolation and introduced into other practical recovery sessions in order for them to be maximally effective.

Chapter 9
Periodisation for Peak Performance

Introduction

Periodisation is the organised division of the overall training programme into periods that accomplish a range of differing, yet cumulative, goals. Periodisation of a competitive programme can be for the athlete's career – a 4-year (quadrennial) plan (eg for Olympic preparation) or an annual plan. According to the theories that have been popularised over the last 20 years, the annual plan is traditionally organised into preparation (pre-season), competition and transition phases (close/off season, active recovery). There are four training cycles used to aid in the planning of the competitive year (Bompa, 1999), as listed below and outlined in more detail in the following sections:

- **Macrocycle**: Usually an annual plan of repeated (yet modified) cycles in the long-term training plan.

- **Mesocycle**: A 3–6-week block of training.

- **Microcyle**: Briefer periods of time, usually consisting of 1-week training blocks.

- **Training Unit**: Individual block of training in pursuit of a training objective.

Macrocycle Design

The training cycles outlined above allow a coach to define the optimal sequence for training emphasis at differing points of the year, so as to maximise potential for competitive performances (a concept known as *peaking*). The macrocycle (typically one year) helps the coach to define the times at which they would like the player's performance to peak. This is achieved by the manipulation of training variables in order to achieve the maximum potential during competitive performances. The number of target competitive peaks in a year depends on the sport, the individual's training age and the individual's competitive schedule. Some sports may require a monocycle (single peak), for example, national or world championships. Others, such as track athletes competing in the indoor and outdoor seasons, may require a bi-cycle (double-peak) plan. These peaks need to be sufficiently far apart to allow the athlete to achieve both.

Conversely, the team-sport performer must try to perform at peak, for a number of successive weeks, over the extended period of a season. This is achieved by manipulation of the training nature, volume and intensity during the training week, following the principles outlined below:

- Recovery should follow performance.

- Heavy training should be built into the early part of the training week.

- Lighter training loads and non-active training (ie classroom-based activities) should feature towards the end of the week/close to competition.

- Recovery and peaking should take place in preparation for the following weekend competition.

However, the basic principles of peaking must also be adopted during out-of-season phases.

Mesocycle Design

Mesocycles allow for the cumulative effects of training series to be maximally beneficial to the performer, and prevent disturbances to the adaptive training process. The goals for each mesocycle should be cumulative (ie build on previous goals and contribute to the goals of the following cycle) so that the objectives of the overall training plan can be met. Therefore, mesocycles are classified according to their objective (Zatsiorski, 1995):

- **Accumulative**: The objective is to improve basic motor abilities (conditioning) as well as sport technique. Training in this phase is not always sport specific and success is often evaluated according to tests.

- **Transmutative**: The objective is to develop activity-specific fitness and polish specific techniques. Progress is evaluated by performance in simulated competitions.

- **Realisational**: The objective is to put on the best performance attainable within defined parameters of competition.

- **Regenerational**: The objective is to allow the performer a period of active recovery away from sport-specific training and competition stressors in order to facilitate recovery.

The duration and format of the realisation phases will vary within, as well as between, games. Tennis players, for example, may have a number of tournaments throughout the year and may frequently play on consecutive days. Typically, the more serious player will have a number of discrete accumulative, transmutative, realisational and regenerational mesocycles in the training year. In contrast, team games such as soccer, rugby and hockey will have a much longer, realisational mesocycle (see Table 9) and may have up to two games a week, but rarely play on consecutive days.

The nature of the competitive phase will determine the periodisation strategy that a coach employs. It is important to identify times when training is given priority, competition is given priority and other times when recovery (the importance of which is highlighted in Chapter 8) is prioritised.

Table 9: Generalised example of training plan for a team game

	General Training	Early Pre-season	Late Pre-season	In-season	Regeneration
Example Dates	End May to mid-June	Mid-June to mid-July	Mid-July to mid-August	Mid-August to start of May	First 3 weeks in May
Strength and Power					
Objectives	Develop strength base.	Develop power base.	Develop maximal power.	Peaking for the weekend.	Cross-training.
Example Methods*	Multi-joint, multi-muscle weight lifting. Sets of 8–10 reps. Combination sets (1 rep of 6–7 exercises put together).	Multi-joint, multi-muscle weight lifting. 12–15 sets of 5 reps. Low-intensity plyometrics.	Multi-joint, multi-muscle weight lifting. 10–14 sets of 3–5 reps. High-intensity, multi-directional plyometrics.	Multi-joint, multi-muscle weight lifting. 8–12 Sets of 3–5 reps. Complex training with multi-directional plyometrics.	Multi-joint, multi-muscle weight lifting. 10–15 sets of 10 reps. Eccentric lifts. Upper- and lower-body split routines.
Endurance					
Objectives	Develop base-line endurance.	Develop tolerance for high-intensity activity.	Match-intensity metabolic conditioning (anaerobic endurance).	Peaking for the weekend.	Cross-training.
Example Methods**	300–400 m intervals. Rowing ergometer.	Lactate generation activities: work:rest ratio of 1:5 Short interval training 50–100 m sprints.	Sport-specific practices work:rest ratio of 1:3 to 1:1 Should include all fatiguing elements of the sport (contact, getting off the floor, jumping, running, etc).	Match-intensity drills. 10–50 m intervals with sport-specific work periods (eg 30–90s duration) with 1:3 to 1:1 work:rest ratio. Fitness integrated into technical and tactical coaching sessions.	Low-intensity activities that avoid impact loading and sport-specific training demands. Examples: water-based activities and cycling.
Speed and Agility					
Objectives	Speed technique work.	Develop maximal speed.	Acceleration and agility work.	Peaking for the weekend.	Cross-training.
Example Methods***	Technique drills. Stride length. Stride frequency.	Top-speed drills. Gear-change sprints.	Acceleration drills. Resisted and assisted running Reaction drills. Sport-specific movement-pattern drills.	Agility drills integrated into warm-ups and technical practices. Complex drills.	Reaction drills. Neuro-muscular firing activities. Non-sport-specific practices.

* Refer to Chapters 4 and 5   ** Refer to Chapter 3   ***Refer to Chapter 6

Mesocycles allow the coach to design a programme that reflects the fact that the development of some athletic abilities is considered prerequisite to others. Training for many sports is multifaceted and requires the development of many training systems. For example, canoeing requires canoeing, running, swimming, weight training and skiing, and specific performance aspects have to be emphasised during certain periods while others are simultaneously stabilised or maintained.

Emphasising one training element over another is known as the practice of conjugative succession of training mesocycles. An old Hungarian saying expresses this in a slightly different manner: 'With one ass you cannot sit on two horses!' (Balyi, 2003). This is because the effects of certain types of training can interfere with each other. For example, strength/power training combined with aerobic training can result in no effect at all, or a slightly positive effect on aerobic endurance, provided there is little gain in body mass. However, the same combination of training methods (strength/power and aerobic training) can also result in attenuated gains in strength, speed and particularly in power. This is because the different types of training target different energy systems and different muscle fibres (Stone and Plisk, 2004). Similarly, the performer will not be able to improve their speed if they are fatigued from other training methods. This also applies to plyometric training: not only will a tired performer not be able to develop the necessary power to perform these exercises, but they could get injured by the high intensity of the training if they are not sufficiently recovered. Therefore, it is important that the coach puts the right training emphasis into the mesocycle at the right time. In the build-up to competition, technical and tactical preparation must take the majority of the coaching time. Therefore, the mesocycles before this should emphasise the fitness development of the performer. Perhaps 80–90% of physical preparation should be done prior to the competitive phase. The process of manipulating training emphasis in response to desired objectives in a cumulative, building process is known as the summative sequencing of training cycles.

Mesocycles allow the coach to investigate the most effective training methods for inducing peak performance, as each stage requires the athlete to achieve a minor performance peak. With the change in emphasis of each session, it can also be realised that mesocycles are motivational to the performer and the coach, allowing interest to be maintained. This realised, the coach should also recognise that competition, playing and training is highly intensive and cannot be maintained at a high level throughout the year. Such training has a strong component of stress, both physically and psychologically.

Phases of stressful activities should be interspersed with periods of recovery and regeneration, during which times the athletes are exposed to less pressure. Some of the more traditionally recognised methods used to design mesocycles can be seen below:

- **Traditional wave theory:** Gradual manipulation of training volume and intensity.

- **Step periodisation:** Abrupt changes in volume and intensity, interspersed with periods of regeneration.

- **Skill–strength periodisation:** Educational phase spent perfecting technical/movement skills before embarking on the development of speed, strength, etc.

- **Emphasis periodisation** (concentration of loading): Each micro-/mesocycle has a specific emphasis, which acts as a foundation for the following training period.

All theories are emergent from the same starting point, which is the needs analysis of the individual athlete or team. The key dates in the programme structure relate to the competitive objectives of the programme, as determined by the coach and the athlete. However, these theories have predominantly been justified by anecdotal evidence, rather than researched fact, largely due to the logistical problems of undertaking such studies.

Microcycle Design

Microcycles are training blocks of between 4 and 8 days, although in most game-based sports these are based around 7 days. Although general training can be planned for a competitive year (as in Table 9), detailed training planning should only be done 1–3 weeks in advance. This is because training and competition can be interrupted by factors such as injury, suspension and other factors. This also allows for coaches to evaluate their training methods, look at what is getting results and manipulate subsequent training sessions accordingly.

Training microcycles (and, in the longer term, mesocycles) should all be designed to follow the principles of training[34]. These principles are derived from a theoretical model known as the *overcompensation cycle*. This model is central to the idea of peaking and it demonstrates that it is only through recovering appropriately from training sessions that the athletic potential of a player can actually improve.

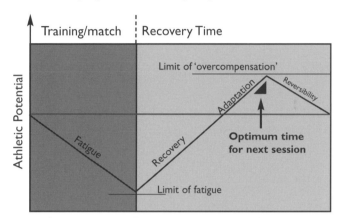

Figure 277: The overcompensation cycle

This is a theoretical model and there are no hard and fast rules for how long each individual will take to reach the point of overcompensation after a specific session. This depends on the nature of the training session and the fitness levels of the individual player concerned – it can take the neuromuscular system up to 6 days to fully recover from some very intense plyometrics sessions, whereas the aerobic and anaerobic metabolic systems may be recovered within 24 hours from some sessions. What is certain is that time to achieve overcompensation can be accelerated by facilitated recovery training/activities. The sooner a player recovers from fatigue, the fresher they will be for training and the better the chances of improving (the aim of coaching). Indeed, the ability of the player to recover from heavy training may be a good indicator for coaches to use as a measure of the success of their training programme. It should also be borne in mind that, while the overcompensation model was originally thought of as a physiological model, it also applies to other performance variables, such as psychology. Reduced psychological drive is very much a direct result (not a side-effect) of fatigue.

It is important to realise that performers cannot progress if they are training at very heavy loads all of the time. Therefore, it is important that a coach varies the workload that a performer is subjected to between microcycles, as well as within them – this is particularly important in the preparation phases. This enables an athlete to experience progressively increased training loads, interspersed with periods of recovery. In a developmental athlete who is getting used to progressively increased training loads, this sequence of microcycles might look like the sequence demonstrated in Figure 278.

In a more advanced performer, the very heavy training loads may come at the start of the 4-week training cycle, when the individual (or team) is able to train with more intensity in a more recovered state. The sequencing of very heavy weeks can be manipulated according to the needs of the programme, although it is recommended that a very heavy training week is always preceded by a medium-intensity training load (Figure 279).

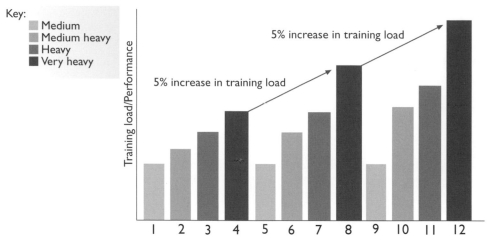

Figure 278: Examples of the manipulation of training loads between weeks in a developmental performer

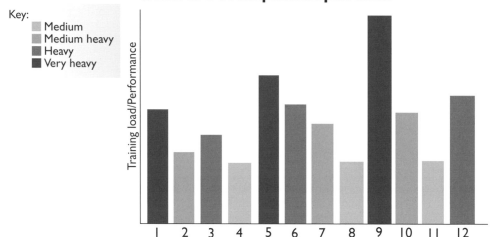

Figure 279: Examples of the manipulation of training loads between weeks in an experienced performer

Tapering is the gradual reduction in training volume (though not necessarily intensity) achieved by decreasing the physical and psychological stressors to the body as the competition period gets closer. Intensity should be maintained, as players need to be able to cope with the demands of competition and these demands, therefore, need to be maintained within training. However, simply reducing the number of repetitions or total training time that the player is exposed to can reduce the training load.

In team games, tapering might involve doing very intense and physical training sessions at the start of the week, then doing some very intense (short duration) technical and tactical practices towards the end of the week. This might be followed by some recovery sessions, or replacing physical training sessions with non-physical ones, such as tactical discussions or performance planning. This tapering of training load should allow the player to go into competition feeling fresh and totally prepared for the competition that follows.

The Training Unit

Microcycles are made up of training sessions, which in turn are made up of training units. A *training unit* is an individual session in pursuit of a specific training objective, within which rest periods are not longer than 30 minutes of a session. There can be a number of training units in a day or indeed within a session (depending on the performance level of the player). This is influenced by the *intra-unit ratio*. This is the loading:recovery ratio within an individual training unit. Sessions with larger training loads need to have a small intra-unit ratio. Similarly, a training session immediately before competition may have a large loading:recovery ratio (ie some very small periods of intense activity followed by longer periods of recovery).

Summary

- Training plans can be designed for between 1 and 4 years at a time, with detailed planning occurring up to 4 weeks in advance.

- The goals of a training session build into those for the week, month, season and training year.

- Periodisation is the process that involves building a training series into a planned sequence that will allow the athlete to achieve optimal performances at key competitions or matches in the season. Identifying and planning for target competitions for a given performer or squad is the starting point for designing any periodised programme.

- The building blocks for a periodised programme are the macrocycle (the competitive year), the mesocycle (blocks of 4–8-week duration, each with a particular objective), the microcycle (usually a training week) and the training unit (individual session with a specific objective).

- Undertaking a needs analysis of the individual athlete or team will enable a coach to determine what a player or team needs to do in order to achieve peak performance in a target competition.

- The foundation theories underpinning periodisation principles have been predominantly justified by anecdotal evidence, rather than researched fact, and therefore the theories are there to be challenged by creative and innovative coaches!

References

Balyi, I. (2003) 'Windows of training opportunity', paper presented at **sport**scotland National Strength and Conditioning Conference, May 2003.

Bompa, T. (1999) *Periodization: Theory and Methodology of Training.* Illinois: Human Kinetics. ISBN: 0-880118-51-2.

Plisk, S. and Stone, M.H. (2003) 'Periodisation strategies', *Strength and Conditioning Journal,* 17: 19–37.

Zatsiorsky, V.M. (1995) *Science and Practice of Strength Training.* Illinois: Human Kinetics. ISBN: 0-873224-74-4.

Further Reading

Galvin, B. and Ledger, P. (1998) *A Guide to Planning Coaching Programmes.* Leeds: Coachwise Solutions/The National Coaching Foundation. ISBN: 1-902523-00-8.*

*Available from Coachwise 1st4sport. For a full range of sports education and training equipment, please visit www.1st4sport.com or call 0113-201 5555.

Notes

1.   Low-intensity exercise is a relative term and depends upon the training state of the individuals concerned.

2.   Typically, the point at which the oxygen supply becomes insufficient occurs at intensities somewhere between 70% and 80% of maximum, depending upon the training status of the player.

3.   Remember that all energy systems work simultaneously.

4.   *Biceps* – Two-headed muscle. *Brachii* – located on the upper arm.

5.   *Triceps* – Three-headed muscle.

6.   The *Quadriceps* group comprises the *Rectus femoris, Vastus medialis, Vastus lateralis* and *Vastus intermedius.*

7.   The *Hamstring* group comprises the *Semimembranosis, Semitendinosis* and *Biceps femoris.*

8. $\dot{V}O_2$ max is the maximum ability to consume oxygen for energy production, while breathing air at sea level.

9.   Agility – changes of direction with maximal efficiency and minimum disruption to velocity.

10.   In some sports, such as tennis, acceleration is the most vital component in this equation. In others, such as rugby union, the strength component is arguably the most vital characteristic.

11.   Court surface and its effect on the bounce have implications for the body position when playing shots; something that should be reflected in the training movements used in conditioning, as illustrated in Chapter 4.

12.   Creatine-phosphate system – energy supply for high-intensity activities lasting 3–10 seconds.

13.   A threshold value for working anaerobically is usually accepted as 4 millimoles.

14.   Running on a grass park or sandy beach is much harder on the muscles, but great for developing proprioception – internal sense of body position – in the muscles.

15.   A similar variation of this exercise can be adopted by the coach, to the same end.

16.   SMARTER – specific, measurable, achievable, relevant, time related, exciting, recorded.

17.   It is recognised that repeated 180° turns are not part of the game of rugby.

18.   Courtesy of Stone, M. (2004) from the **sport**scotland National Strength and Conditioning Conference. Adapted from Häkkinen and Komi (1985) in the *Scandinavian Journal of Sports Science* 7(2): 55–64 and 65–76.

19.   Kinesiology is the study of joint and muscle actions in movement.

20.   Closed-kinetic-chain exercises are when the body has a point in contact with the ground.

21   Countermovements are movements in one direction followed by movement in the opposite direction, thus initiating the all-important plyometrics (ie stretch shortening) reflex response for optimum power development.

22   For more information on this, the coach is recommended to follow the protocols and accreditation procedures recommended by the United Kingdom Strength and Conditioning Association (see Useful Contacts section, page 183).

23   The principles relating to the major steps of the lift are: head up, chest high, shoulder blades pulled back, normally straight back, trunk and gluteal musculature pulled tight and knees moving along the same line as the toes.

24   Diagram adapted from Fleck and Kraemer, 1997.

25   At certain times, it is important to get the balance right between lifting heavy and lifting explosively.

26   The player should be able to see the big toe on the inside of the knee as it is bent into the squat position upon landing.

27   Correct sprinting technique: the body mechanics that result in the best combination of stride length and stride frequency for producing maximum sprinting velocity in a given instance.

28   A reaction ball is a rubber ball with angled, uneven surfaces to produce unpredictable bounce direction.

29   Training too hard is overdoing the intensity rather than the effort. This is known as acute over-reaching and can be associated with an injury to the musculo-skeletal system.

30   DOMS is a common phenomenon experienced by many who have been in sport for any great length of time.

31   A serious competitor is recommended to get no more than between seven and nine hours' sleep a night.

32   The Likert scale poses a question and elicits a response on a scale, such as Strongly Agree – Agree – Undecided – Disagree – Strongly Disagree.

33   Pain has a protective purpose in limiting physical activity on any injury site.

34   The principles of training are: progression, overload, specificity, recovery and reversibility.

Bibliography

Alter, M.J. (2005) *Sport Stretch*. Illinois: Human Kinetics. ISBN: 0-880118-23-7.

Baechle, T. and Earle, R. (eds) (2000) *Essentials of Strength Training and Conditioning*. Illinois: Human Kinetics. ISBN: 0-736000-89-5.

Balyi, I. (2003) 'Windows of training opportunity', paper presented at **sport**scotland National Strength and Conditioning Conference, May 2003.

Bean, A. (2003) *The Complete Guide to Sports Nutrition*. London: A & C Black. ISBN: 0-713653-89-2.*

Bompa, T. (1999) *Periodization: Theory and Methodology of Training*. Illinois: Human Kinetics. ISBN: 0-880118-51-2.

Brewer, C., Favre, M. and Low, L. (2005) 'Weight lifting for sports specific benefits', http://www.coachesinfo.com/category/strength_and_conditioning/

Brewer, C. and Stone, M.H. (2005) 'Coaching the double knee bend', http://www.coachesinfo.com/category/strength_and_conditioning/

Brown, L., Ferrigno, V. and Santana, J. C. (2000) *Training for Speed, Agility and Quickness*. Illinois: Human Kinetics. ISBN: 0-736002-39-1.*

Byrd, R., Baker, C., Pierce, K. and Brady, J. (2004) 'Young weightlifters' performance across time', http://www.coachesinfo.com/category/strength_and_conditioning/245

Christmass, M.A., Richmond, S.E., Cable, N.T. and Hartmann, P.E. (1995) 'A metabolic characterisation of singles tennis' in *Science and Racket Sports II* (1998) Lees, A., Maynard, I., Hughes, M. and Reilly, T. (eds). London: E. & F. N. Spon. ISBN: 0-419230-30-0.

Chu, D.A. (1996) *Explosive Power and Strength: Complex Training for Maximal Results*. Illinois: Human Kinetics. ISBN: 0-873226-43-7.

Coachwise 1st4sport (2001) *Speed Training Drills* video. Leeds: Coachwise 1st4sport.*

Crosland, J. (2005) *Fuelling Performers*. Leeds: Coachwise Business Solutions/The National Coaching Foundation. ISBN: 1-902523-23-7.*

Elliott, B., Dawson, B. and Pyke, F. (1985) 'The ergogenics of singles tennis', *Journal of Human Movement Studies* 11: 11–20.

Farrally, M. (2003) *An Introduction to the Structure of the Body*. Leeds: Coachwise Business Solutions/The National Coaching Foundation. ISBN: 1-850601-69-0.*

Farrally, M. (2005) *An Introduction to Sports Physiology*. Leeds: Coachwise Business Solutions/The National Coaching Foundation. ISBN: 1-902523-65-2.*

Fleck, S.J. and Kraemer, W.J. (1997) *Designing Resistance Training Programmes*. Illinois: Human Kinetics. ISBN: 0-873221-13-3.

Galvin, B. and Ledger, P. (1998) *A Guide to Planning Coaching Programmes*. Leeds: Coachwise Solutions/The National Coaching Foundation. ISBN: 1-902523-00-8.*

International Tennis Federation (2000). *Rules of Tennis*. London: ITF Ltd.

Meir, R., Colla, P. and Milligan, C. (2001) 'Impact of the 10-meter rule change on professional rugby league: implications for training.' *Strength and Conditioning Journal* 23 (6): 42–6.

Pearson, A. (2003) *Dynamic Flexibility*. A & C Black. ISBN: 0-713664-52-5.*

Pearson, A. and Hawkins, D. (2005) *SAQ Youth*. A & C Black. ISBN: 0-713670-42-8.*

Plisk, S. and Stone, M.H. (2003) 'Periodisation strategies', *Strength and Conditioning Journal* 17: 19–37.

Reilly, T. and Palmer, J. (1995) 'Investigation of exercise intensity in male tennis single/lawn tennis' in *Science and Racket Sports II*, Lees, A., Maynard, I., Hughes, M. and Reilly, T. (eds). London: E. and F. N. Spon. ISBN: 0-419230-30-0.

Siff, M. (2003) *Supertraining*. Supertraining Institute. ISBN: 1-874856-65-6.

Stafford, I. (2004) *Coaching for Long-term Athlete Development*. Leeds: Coachwise Business Solutions/The National Coaching Foundation. ISBN: 1-902523-70-9*

Stone, M.H. (1990) 'Muscle conditioning and muscle injuries', *Medicine & Science in Sport & Exercise*. 22 (4) 457–62.

Stone, M.H. (2000) 'Explosive exercise and training', *National Strength and Conditioning Association Journal*, 15 (3): 7–15.

Stone, M.H. (2002) 'How strong is strong enough?', http://www.coachesinfo.com/article/index.php?id=246&style=printable

Stone, M.H. (2005) 'The use of weightlifting pulling movements in sports', paper presented at The UK Strength and Conditioning Association Conference, Loughborough, May 2005.

Thompson, C.W. and Floyd, R.T. (eds) (2003) *Manual of Structural Kinesiology*. New York: McGraw-Hill Education. ISBN: 0-071218-38-6.

Zatsiorsky, V.M. (1995) *Science and Practice of Strength Training*. Illinois: Human Kinetics. ISBN: 0-873224-74-4.

* Available from Coachwise 1st4sport. For a full range of sports education and training equipment, please visit www.1st4sport.com or call 0113-201 5555.

Glossary

Acceleration: Time between starting a movement and reaching top speed.

Adipose tissue: Tissue adapted to store lipids (fats) as high-density energy storage.

Aerobic: With oxygen. For example, *aerobic endurance* – the ability to sustain performance-producing energy using oxygen.

Agility: The ability to change direction or body position with the maximum efficiency.

All or nothing principle: Motor units in muscle contraction are either activated or they are not.

Anaerobic: Without oxygen.

Antagonistic muscles: Muscles that oppose a prime mover (agonist) for a given movement.

Ballistic stretches: Forceful, explosive stretching movements that utilise momentum and velocity to increase the range of movement.

Bioenergetics: The process of energy production to fuel muscular movement.

Burn-out: A negative/damaged physical or psychological state experienced by an athlete who has been overexposed to training and competition stimuli without due recovery. Often associated with injury, overtraining and unexplained underperformance.

Closed-kinetic-chain exercises: Exercises whereby the body has a point in contact with the ground.

Cognitive: Using mental action or acquiring knowledge through thought, experience and the senses.

Complex training: Using maximal-strength lifts to increase the power or effect of plyometric exercise.

Concentric muscle actions: When one or both myotendinous ends of the muscle (ie the tendon joining muscle to bone) move towards each other and the muscle is shortened during the contraction.

Contrast training: Slow or controlled movements (confined by, for example, a bungee, technique ladder or weight resistance) followed by unrestrained, explosive movements.

Dorsiflex: Pulling the toes towards the knees.

Dynamic stretching: A potentially injurious form of stretching in which a player bounces quickly in a given position in order to lengthen the muscle.

Eccentric muscle action: When the muscle is actively lengthened while contracted. A muscle can only be lengthened by a greater opposing force, as it cannot actively lengthen by itself.

Enzymatic reactions: Enzymes are proteins that accelerate the rate of certain biochemical reactions. They are not changed or spent in the reaction. The concentration of specific enzymes involved in energy systems determines athletic ability.

Extension: Increasing the inner angle of a joint.

Flexion: Decreasing the inner angle of a joint.

Glycolysis: The process of breaking down glycogen or glucose into pyruvate, when it will either be reduced to hydrogen and lactate (fast glycolysis) or, in the presence of oxygen, be taken into the mitochondria to produce ATP.

Hyperextension: A greater-than-normal extension in a joint or series of joints.

Hyperflexion: A greater-than-normal flexion in a joint.

Intra-unit ratio: The loading:recovery ratio within an individual training unit.

Isometric muscle actions: *Iso* – same, *metric* – length. A type of contraction whereby the force generated by the muscle is equal to the resistive mass opposing it and so the muscle remains the same length while contracting.

Kinesiology: The study of joint and muscle actions in movement.

Lactate: The end product of fast glycolysis.

Lactate tolerance: Popular term relating to the ability of the muscle fibres to maintain contractions and enzyme reactions in an acidic environment, caused by a build-up of lactate and hydrogen ions after anaerobic exercise.

Macrocycle: Usually an annual plan of repeated (yet modified) cycles in the long-term training plan (periodisation).

Mesocycle: A 3–6-week block of training within the long-term training plan (periodisation).

Microcycle: Usually these consist of 1-week training blocks, within the long-term training plan (periodisation).

Millimoles: A thousandth of a mole. A mole is the standard unit for an amount of a substance expressed as its molecular weight (in grams).

Mitochondria: The powerhouses of the cell. Their major responsibility is to produce energy, in the presence of oxygen, to power muscle contractions.

Movement time: Time from the beginning of movement to its completion.

Neuromuscular: Nerves and the muscles they supply.

Overcompensation cycle: The theoretical model of training–fatigue–recovery that underpins training-programme structure.

Oxidative phosphorylation: A server of metabolic process, which removes hydrogen from transport substances to produce ATP in the presence of oxygen.

Peaking: The manipulation of training variables in order to ensure optimal readiness for competitive performance.

Periodisation: A planned training schedule of a year's duration, made up of periods or cycles that are often of differing durations, ie macrocycles, mesocycles, microcycles and training units.

Plyometric: Specialist bounding and rebounding exercises that utilise the stretch–shortening cycle to enable a muscle to reach maximum force production in minimum time.

Postural control: Maintaining control of the spine, pelvic and shoulder girdles in relation to the head, knees and ankles.

Prime movers (agonist): Muscles that are responsible for the initiation of a particular movement.

Pronate: Inward rotation of a joint.

Proprioception: Internal sensory mechanism that informs the athlete where all the components of the body are, in relation to each other, at any one time.

Range of movement (ROM): The degree of movement available around a joint or a series of joints in the body – the key component of flexibility.

Reaction time: Time taken to detect and respond to a stimulus.

Repetition maximum: The maximum number of repetitions that can be completed with a given load.

Size principle of motor unit recruitment: Recruitment sequence of Type I, IIa and IIx fibres in response to the resistive load.

Stabiliser muscles: Muscles working in opposition in any given movement often act as stabilising agents.

Static stretching: A form of stretching in which a position is held for a given duration (usually 6–60 seconds).

Stretching: The training method that enables flexibility (range of movement) to be developed.

Stretch–shortening cycle: Reflex concentric muscle contraction caused by the stretch receptor in the muscle fibre detecting the fibre being stretched forcefully.

Synergistic muscles: Muscles that can indirectly assist the prime movers.

Tapering: A reduction in training volume (not intensity) as competition approaches, in order to enable peaking to occur.

Top speed: Maximum running speed in a player, reached after about 25 metres of movement.

Type I fibres: Slow-twitch muscle fibres.

Type IIa fibres: Fast-twitch intermediate fibres able to work aerobically or anaerobically.

Type IIx fibres: Very explosive fast-twitch anaerobic fibres.

Weight lifting: The use of weight-lifting movements in training for sports performance.

Weightlifting: A recognised Olympic sport, the objective of which is to perform maximally in the snatch, clean, and jerk lifts.

Work:rest ratio: Designated time interval between periods of work and recovery.

$\dot{V}O_2$ *max*: The maximum ability to consume oxygen (for energy production) while breathing air at sea level.

Useful Contacts

sports coach UK

sports coach UK (**scUK**) works closely with sport's governing bodies and other partners to provide a comprehensive service for coaches throughout the UK. This includes an extensive programme of workshops, which have proved valuable to coaches from all types of sports and every level of experience.

For further details of **scUK** workshops in your area, contact the **scUK** Business Support Centre (BSC):

Post: **sports coach UK** Business Support Centre
Sports Development Centre
Loughborough University
Loughborough
Leicestershire LE11 3TU

Tel: 01509-226 130

Fax: 01509-226 134

Email: bsc@sportscoachuk.org

Website: www.sportscoachuk.org/improve/workshop/search.asp

For more details about other membership services such as insurance, contact the **scUK** Headquarters:

Post: **sports coach UK** Headquarters
114 Cardigan Road
Headingley
Leeds LS6 3BJ

Tel: 0113-274 4802

Fax: 0113-275 5019

Email: coaching@sportscoachuk.org

Website: www.sportscoachuk.org

UK Strength and Conditioning Association

Post: 86 Nelson Road
London SW19 1HX

Tel: 0870-116 1566

Fax: 0870-116 1223

Email: info@uksca.org.uk

Website: www.uksca.org.uk

Mission Statement

Our Vision

To have high-quality coaches and coaching interactions operating at every level within sport, contributing to an increase in participation, enjoyment and success in sport

*Better coaches…better coaching…better sport
…more and better participants*

Key components will be:

 a UK Coaching Certificate recognised as world leading in the qualification and continuous professional development of coaches

 a fit-for-purpose coaching workforce from grass roots to high performance across the UK, with the capacity, capability and quality to provide a sustained increase in sports participation and success in sports performance

 a high-quality coaching workforce with a culture of innovation and continuous professional development, with ethical values

 volunteer coaches, valued and nurtured, working alongside a career structure of professional coaches at community, club and performance levels of sport

 a coaching workforce that is representative of the local community in which it operates and the population

 a coaching workforce with the appropriate skills to use sport as a tool to support health, education and social inclusion objectives

Our Purpose

To lead the development of high-quality coaches via the provision of innovative products, services and expert guidance who are fit for purpose and readily available (right place, right time) to increase participation, performance and enjoyment in sport.